ALLEN NEWELL

THE NEW UTOPIANS
A STUDY OF SYSTEM
DESIGN AND SOCIAL CHANGE

PRENTICE-HALL INTERNATIONAL, INC., *London*
PRENTICE-HALL OF AUSTRALIA, PTY., LTD., *Sydney*
PRENTICE-HALL OF CANADA, LTD., *Toronto*
PRENTICE-HALL OF INDIA (PRIVATE) LTD., *New Delhi*
PRENTICE-HALL OF JAPAN, INC., *Tokyo*

THE NEW UTOPIANS

A STUDY OF SYSTEM
DESIGN AND SOCIAL CHANGE

Robert Boguslaw

PRENTICE-HALL, INC.
Englewood Cliffs, N.J.

© 1965 BY

PRENTICE-HALL, INC., ENGLEWOOD CLIFFS, N.J.

Library of Congress
Catalog Card No. 65–19764

PRINTED IN THE UNITED STATES OF AMERICA
62013 – C

PREFACE

This essay was begun as a relatively straightforward description of problems in the analysis and design of contemporary large-scale computer-based command and control systems. It was addressed to the professionals who work together as more or less interdisciplinary teams on terrestrial and extraterrestrial large-scale systems projects—to those who call themselves system engineers, computer programmers, operations researchers, and the like. These are the persons who link the peoples of the world together in communication networks; insure the timely production, transportation, and distribution of bananas, beeswax, and bombs; and increasingly use high-speed digital computers in the process.

But it was not long before I became more and more impressed with the similarity between the intellectual underpinnings of the modern materials I was using and the formulations of social theorists in the Utopian tradition who analyzed existing social systems and designed new ones. I saw that modern system designers were unconsciously treading well-worn paths—that they were embracing the most fundamental errors of earlier efforts and were incorporating them into the fabric of even the most sophisticated of pushbutton systems.

The current preoccupation with computer-based systems and automation has, unfortunately, left the contemporary social scientist, together with the overwhelming majority of our population, occupying the role of bystander. His characteristic involvement in system design efforts is ex post facto, and this greatly circumscribes the range of his possible influence on the design of these crucially significant frames for social behavior.

But the issues involved are much too critical to remain exclusively the preoccupation of our new utopians. What are the characteristics of technology and system design that shape the possibilities for social change in a given society? What characteristics of social change

v

define the possible parameters for technological development and system design? In the face of all this, how *does* one proceed to design a successful system—or a utopia?

I have discussed some of the ideas contained in this book with many friends and colleagues over a period of years. I owe them all a debt of gratitude for their wisdom, patience, encouragement, and advice. Many of them, I am sure, are not aware of the extent to which they have helped. The names that come immediately to mind include: Professors Allen Newell and Herbert A. Simon of Carnegie Institute of Technology, Professor John L. Kennedy of Princeton University, Professor William C. Biel of the University of Southern California, Dr. Robert L. Chapman of Hughes Aircraft Corporation, Dr. George R. Bach of Claremont College, Professors Henry J. Meyer and Ashley C. Weeks of the University of Michigan, Professor Sol Levine of Harvard University, Professor Harold Garfinkel of UCLA, Professor John James of Portland State College, Professor John T. Gullahorn of Michigan State University, Mr. Jeremiah Kaplan, and many, many others, including Mr. Al W. Goodyear, of Prentice-Hall, Inc., who persuaded me to write the book.

Professor James G. March, of Carnegie Institute of Technology, read several chapters of an earlier version and provided penetrating and extremely valuable criticism. I am especially indebted to my friend and colleague, Dr. Robert H. Davis, of the System Development Corporation, who carefully read the entire manuscript and provided detailed comments and suggestions on virtually every page. I also wish to acknowledge the sensitive editing insights of Mr. Joseph Maher and the diligence of Mrs. Dollie Giffin and Mrs. Barbara Meier, who typed the manuscript—several times.

It goes without saying that none of the persons mentioned is to be held responsible for any controversial opinions I may have expressed or for defects of any kind contained in the manuscript.

Finally, I must acknowledge the intangible yet completely indispensable support and assistance provided in a thousand ways by my wife Wanda and our children Rochelle, Janet, and Lisa on the long weekends and evenings when the book was being written.

R.B.

CONTENTS

Chapter 4

HEURISTIC DESIGNS   71

Chapter 5

OPERATING UNIT DESIGNS   99

Chapter 6

AD HOC DESIGNS   127

Chapter 7

WHICH APPROACH IS BEST?   161

Chapter 8

THE POWER OF SYSTEMS AND SYSTEMS OF POWER   181

Index   205

To
MOM and POP

THE UTOPIAN TRADITION
AND AUTOMATION

Utopia is a place that seems to belong either to the past or to the future, and we tend to think of utopians as being either starry-eyed philosophers or wild-eyed reformers. But there is a new breed of utopians afoot, threatening to rush down all the exciting pathways and blind alleys frequented by utopians since the days of Plato. These are the people who are known by such titles as system engineer, computer manufacturer, operations researcher, computer programmer, data processing specialist, or, more simply, system designer.

This book deals with some of the problems confronting these new utopians—the social engineers of our times. But, perhaps much more to the point, it deals with some of the problems they are in the process of preparing for the rest of us.

Most of the new utopians would be either amused or shocked at being called "social engineers." They would almost certainly reject the suggestion that the way they think or the way they act is in any sense "utopian." Computer manufacturers are businessmen. They invest millions of dollars to make a profit in what some of them hope is a competitive market. Computer programmers do what they are told—by the customer or some other boss. System engineers and operations researchers are objective scientists or quasi-scientists. Do these constitute our new breed of utopians? Are these the social engineers of our times?

Yes.

One of the more familiar elements of utopian thought is the aspiration to transcend present reality. This aspiration is normally seen as something less than a dream but more that a simple acceptance of the status quo. Utopians are builders who reject their contemporary status quos and reach out for new forms within which to shape their wished-for worlds. David Riesman once described utopia as a plan that now is nowhere but that someday may be somewhere. In the contemporary world, this utopian "plan" has become known as the process of "system design."

But utopian thinking embraces much more than a plan. It contains the implicit notion that societies must be built free from human imperfections. The classical utopians tried to achieve this end by populating their social systems with perfect human beings, perfect social structures, perfect situations, or perfect principles. They were do-gooders in the finest sense of the term. They desperately wished to escape from the melancholy world in which they lived into a happier, more moral, more just, or more prosperous one. Their primary concern was people—although some focused their efforts upon saving souls while others focused on filling stomachs.

But the new utopians are concerned with non-people and with people-substitutes. Their planning is done with computer hardware, system procedures, functional analyses, and heuristics. We shall examine all these in some detail as we proceed with our discussion. Impatience with "human error" has become a unifying imperative among the new utopians. The theoretical and practical solutions they seek call increasingly for decreases in the number and in the scope of responsibility of human beings within the operating structures of their new machined systems.

In the face of this burgeoning utopian renaissance, social theory has remained an after-the-physical-fact kind of theory. It begins with an acceptance of the status quo in such areas as the facts of our physical environment, human physiology, and the state or projected state of machine technology. It considers the requirements for food, shelter, reproduction, and recreation in the light of this status quo and proceeds to explain how human groups can or do adapt to the world in which they find themselves. The principles, empirical conclusions, theories, hypotheses, and notions that then appear are post hoc. The world of physical reality becomes the constant to which social theory must adapt. Social science becomes, therefore, a very conservative intellectual force on the contemporary scene. In a world of rapid changes in the technology and utilization of high-speed computers, this conservatism takes the form of a concern with the *consequences* that advances in automation will have for such things as family life, employment, juvenile delinquency, community organization, leisure, and educational practice. Studies describing the consequences of introducing automatic equipment in a specific factory, industry, or office become increasingly more abundant. Concern is expressed about the social dislocations arising from mass unemployment. Problems involved in the retraining of workers whose skills have been made obsolete by automatic equipment receive increasing attention from psychologists, sociologists, and economists.

But these questions seldom, if ever, get posed or analyzed *prior* to the construction of large-scale machined systems. They simply do not appear on the checklist of variables characteristically used by system engineers engaged in the design process. These variables reflect a perspective of utilitarian efficiency. They specifically do *not* stem from a perspective that views human beings as human beings. This is not, of course, to deny that the utilitarian perspective is ultimately rationalized as serving long-range humanist ends. The point is that the advent of machined systems does result and is resulting in dislocation of human beings, unemployment, and short-run social problems. It is precisely in the short run that our new utopias continually fail to fulfill expectations.

And so it is that the new utopians retain their aloofness from human and social problems presented by the fact or threat of machined systems and automation. They are concerned with neither souls nor stomachs. People problems are left to the after-the-fact efforts of social scientists. And there is, of course, no dearth of effort addressed by social scientists to the problems presented by the fact or threat of automation. The significant feature of virtually all this effort is that even its most venturesome probes begin with an unquestioning acceptance of the technological status quo. The very real danger that arises is the salient one that contemporary and future populations will be wagged increasingly by their technological tails.

System engineers and system designers characteristically address themselves to a quite different set of problems. Their concern is with "hardware," "equipment," and "equipment systems." Their task is characteristically pictured as the making of decisions involving alternate choices of equipment or the optimum use of equipment that has already been installed. Their tasks revolve about these choices. Their world is the world of automated equipment.

Let us for a moment examine in more detail precisely what automated equipment is required to do. Suppose you are a design engineer who wants to construct an automatic or robot driver for a standard automobile. You might begin by analyzing the characteristic behaviors of large numbers of human operators. Switching on the ignition, touching the self-starter, releasing the brake, and so forth would quickly be seen as routine operations that could be listed as standard operating procedures and included in a computer program to control and order the behavior of the robot. At another level of analysis, it would be necessary to codify traffic regulations and provide a means for the robot to sense the existence of situations in which a specific rule must be applied. Thus, for example, you might give the automatic operator sensory equipment to permit recognition of a red traffic signal, stop sign, or traffic policeman's whistle. At a third level of analysis, you might codify appropriate local rules of courtesy to insure that the automatic operator did not, for example, emerge as a big city boor when driving through small towns.

Somewhere in your efforts as a design engineer you will be forced inevitably to draw the line on incorporation of niceties because of the sheer limit of memory available in the computer equipment at any one moment of time. For example, do you permit the robot to pick up hitchhikers? What do you do if your robot has the right of way but finds that another driver is illegally denying it to him? How does he decide between crashing into a group of children playing on the sidewalk and a group of teen-agers crossing the street? What about a group of senior citizens?

The point, of course, is a simple one. In the language of sociology, the tasks set for these computerized equipment systems prescribe behavior patterns within a social system. Any computer program or hardware complex that sets forth operational procedures is, in fact, specifying details of permissible social action. Behaviors not specified are more than illegal—they are not possible. All this does not imply, however, that outcomes unknown to the designer cannot take place within a computerized system. We shall take up this point at some length in connection with heuristic programming. For the moment, however, it is important to understand that our concern is not with toys, gadgets, or advertising copy versions of a housewife's paradise filled with automated dishwashers and potato peelers. Large-scale industrial, military, and space systems are the new utopias that the age of computers has thrust upon us.

These utopias contain all the critical features of classical utopias save one. They are designed to deal with some perceived limitation in the existing organization of men and materials, they attempt to improve an existing state of affairs, and they frequently are utterly visionary in concept and disappointing in execution. They lack only the humanoid orientation characteristic of all classical utopian schemes.

These new utopias resemble classical utopias in their approaches to system design; in their assumptions about system states, system environments, operating units, and operating principles; in the quest of their designers for operating modes free from human imperfections; in their foibles and in their strengths. They differ from the classical variety primarily in the scope of their operations. The major limiting factor that defined the scope of classical utopias was the relatively unambiguous one of geography. Volumes could be written (and are, indeed) about alternate social and physical arrangements within a circumscribed geographical region. The goals, operations, and customs that could be prescribed or designed for these societies were limited only by the imagination or good judgment of their designers. The new utopians, on the contrary, seem to have no spatial limits but are much more rigorously confined in function. They tend to deal with man only in his workaday world without prescribing sex practices, childrearing procedures, or methods for achieving the good life. They deal with messages, decisions, commands, and work procedures. They involve plans for orbiting the earth as well as the neighboring planets. They receive their impetus from the newly discovered capabilities of computational equipment rather than from the fundamental moral, intellectual, or even physical requirements of mankind. These are the utopias that are well along on the drawing boards of system designers throughout the contemporary world. They are the systems that are being planned and constructed in the utopian renaissance.

The design orientation of these contemporary systems can probably best be described as functional analysis. What is to be required of the system? What functions will it serve? What components will it include? What tasks will be assigned to these components? These are the critical questions to be asked in functional analyses.

The functional analysis of systems has had a very long history. We may observe a truly classical case in point by noting the procedures followed by Socrates as Plato has him design a State. In *The Republic*, Socrates begins by establishing the notion that the State arises from the needs of mankind. Many needs exist, and many individuals possessing varying skills are required to fill them. We each require partners and helpers. When these partners and helpers are assembled within one area, we have a State. Since the State is invented out of necessity, Socrates proceeds to enumerate the necessities involved. The first three are food, housing, and clothing—in that order. The personnel subsystem suggested to Socrates by this enumeration includes a husbandman, a builder, and a weaver. On second thought, Socrates throws in a shoemaker and some other miscellaneous menials. Even in this bare framework, problems of division of labor immediately arise, and Socrates rapidly concludes that each man ought to do only those things he does best.

Very rapidly the necessity for toolmakers, carpenters, smiths, shepherds, importers, exporters, merchants, and so forth, becomes apparent—even for existence on a primitive level. To establish a truly civilized State, one must include actors, dancers, dressmakers, servants, tutors, and finally perhaps a slice of land belonging to a neighbor. This, together with the necessity for protecting one's own land from neighbors who wish a slice of *it*, leads to the recognition of the possibility of war and the necessity for an army. Since war is an art, requiring a long apprenticeship, the necessity for selecting a warrior class—the guardians—arises.

And so although Plato is by no means to be considered a narrow or mechanistic thinker, his designer, Socrates, sketches the components for a well-functioning state and provides us with a blueprint describing how to assemble these components to form an ideal Republic. Plato was not, of course, alone in his use of functional analysis to design systems. From Sir Thomas More to George Orwell, utopians have provided carefully conceived functional analyses for their utopian systems. They have, however, given relatively little, if any, attention to the nature of the situations within which their utopias were to operate. Let us take a moment to examine this problem.

ESTABLISHED AND EMERGENT SITUATIONS

If we distinguish a continuum of situations in which action can occur, we may call one pole of this continuum "established" and the other pole "emergent." An established situation is one in which all action-relevant environmental conditions are specifiable and predictable; all action-relevant states of the system are specifiable and predictable; available research technology or records are adequate to provide statements about the probable consequences of alternative actions. In contrast, an emergent

situation is one in which some of these conditions do not prevail.[1]
It is probably some implicit notion of the distinction between
these two kinds of situation that gives rise to perennial discussions about the relative virtues of "book learning" and "experience." When someone asserts that he has "experience" as
compared with "book learning," his assertion may be translated
into something like the following: "The situations you have
studied in your texts and laboratories are *established* situations.
The situations I have to deal with in everyday life are *emergent*.
Your thorough understanding of established situations is worthless
for the things that are really problems to me in every-day life."

If the speaker happens to be a businessman, or a labor
leader, or a governmental official, or a military leader, he would
be apt to have much the same reaction—and appropriately so—to
designers of established situation utopias or systems.

A multiplication table is an established situation. So is a table
of random numbers. A controlled laboratory experiment is devoted to the study of established situations. A five-alarm fire is an
established situation—for a well-organized fire department. Most
of the work done by unskilled or semiskilled labor probably deals
with established situations. A sample attitude survey of a population with previously determined characteristics is established
situation analysis.

Painting a masterpiece of art involves dealing with an emergent situation—as does creating the mutiplication table or the
random number table before such things existed, or reacting to a
fire in your bedroom, or playing chess in the middle game. (Winning a "book" ending in chess calls for action in an established
situation.) Making a business or political or military decision in
the absence of staff work that has provided probability statements
for alternate decisions requires the ability to deal with emergent
situations. Building a social, political, or military system to provide world peace and prosperity within an environment subject
to constant and unpredicted change—or within an environment of
such complexity that available analytic techniques cannot provide

---

[1] Robert Boguslaw, "Situation Analysis and the Problem of Action,"
Social Problems, VIII, No. 3 (Winter 1961), 212–219.

reasonable probability statements—requires emergent situation design.

But what, specifically, do we mean by emergent or established system design? To answer this question, it is first necessary to distinguish several varieties of system design.

APPROACHES TO SYSTEM DESIGN

In the following chapter we shall explore contemporary connotations of the word *system*. For the moment, however, we are concerned with the design process. To begin with, it is important to observe that some systems may be required to deal only with established situations; others may be required to deal only with emergent situations; still others may be required to deal with both established and emergent situations. But, suppose you wished to prepare a checklist of things to be included within your design—what would you do?

Different system designers characteristically begin their work not only with queries about system functions but with different answers to questions such as the following: What is the problem you are trying to solve? Why are you trying to solve it? What *kind* of solution would you accept as satisfactory? How much time and effort are you prepared to devote to the enterprise? How enduring must your solution be?

Differences in the approach to system design involve implicit if not explicit differences in these answers. They also imply gross differences in methodology and technique. We may distinguish four approaches to system design used by both the classical and the new utopians. They are the Formalist Approach, the Heuristic Approach, the Operating Unit Approach, and the Ad Hoc Approach.

I. *The Formalist Approach.* The formalist approach is characterized by the implicit or explicit use of models. It has been suggested[2] that there are only two basic kinds of models—replica and symbolic. Replica models provide a pictorial representation.

---

[2] Alphonse Chapanis, "Men, Machines, and Models," *American Psychologist*, XVI, No. 3 (March 1961), 115–116.

They are material or tangible and look like the real thing. Examples include such things as toy automobiles or models of an interplanetary rocket. Symbolic models are intangible. They use ideas, concepts, and abstract symbols to represent objects. They don't even resemble the real thing. They use lines and arrows to symbolize information flow and things like diagrammatic blocks to symbolize major elements of a system. Mathematical models are simply a subclass of these symbolic models.

A recent text[3] on operations research attempts to clarify the role of mathematical models in this field by suggesting an analogy to mechanics. The physics student who is given a series of propositions about the behavior of ideal systems finds that these propositions when expressed in mathematical symbology form a model of the world of reality. This model can be manipulated more easily than the real world itself and is therefore useful. Thus, Newton's laws of motion, together with the concept of friction that opposes motion, provide a model that more or less accurately accounts for many observable phenomena in our world. It is recognized, of course, that some things cannot be explained by this model and that additional variables such as air resistance, earth rotation, electrostatic charges, and the like, may have to be included to solve special problems. But this is trivial—presumably each succeeding variable leads simply to a greater complexity in analysis.

An informative illustration of this approach is found not only in the work of such new utopians as contemporary mathematical model builders and operations researchers but also in the work of many classical utopians as well. The resemblance between the efforts of an old-fashioned utopian such as Charles Fourier and the endeavors of contemporary formalist designers is striking. Fourier's design techniques were meticulous, painstaking, and highly rational, if one is prepared to grant him certain basic assumptions about the situations within which his system would be required to operate. The charge that he was also probably somewhat mad constitutes a critique of his assumptions rather

---

[3] Maurice Sasieni, Arthur Yaspan, and Lawrence Friedman, *Operations Research—Methods and Problems* (New York: John Wiley & Sons, Inc., 1959).

than of his logic. Like his contemporary counterparts, he was a prodigious classifier possessed with what one can only call a passion for precision, planning, and order. On the contemporary system designer job market he would indubitably be called a detail man par excellence.

Fourier[4] provides us with not only a description of the buildings to be used in his system but also a budget and several other niceties as well. His assumptions include an analysis of the characteristics of the human components of his system. He assumes that these characteristics are stable and sufficiently clear-cut to serve as the elements of the system. He makes the specific assumption that all men are not created equal—at least insofar as their innate qualities or capacities are concerned. His task is essentially the engineering one of designing a system when given a specification of the situations with which his system will have to deal. His model is a pictorial one done in words.

Fourier is a man with a design package to peddle. He was much less successful than his contemporary counterparts. To the day of his death he waited for a potential client with sufficient capital and interest to fund his plan, and, it must be confessed, it was a rather complete if not a truly tidy package that he had to offer. In brief, on a contemporary design proposal, it might be presented in something like the following terms:

Phalanx—System Design

A. *Function* (mission): Establish and indefinitely maintain a prototype agricultural community (phalanx).

B. *Performance Requirements:*

   1. Operational:

     a) The entire system must be self-sustaining within one year of operational start date.

     b) The system must provide sufficient food, clothing, shelter, and amusement for 1800 people. "Sufficient" is defined as meaning more than the minimum required for good health and happiness as measured by ongoing surveys described below.

---

[4] Charles Fourier, *Theory of Social Organization* (New York: C. P. Somerby, 1876).

    c) Buildings described in Annex I must be built according to specification.

  2. The system will be part of a modularized world-wide system. Its operations must be fully compatible with 2,985,983 other phalanxes to be subsequently established. It must not siphon off resources of other phalanxes.

C. *Inputs From Other Systems:* It must require no inputs whatsoever from other systems one year after operational date.

D. *Constraints:*

  1. Physical Environment:

  Tract land three miles square. Tract will be watered by a stream. Surface will be undulating and adaptable to a great variety of branches of agriculture.

  2. Resource Constraints:

    a) No more than 1800 members.

    b) Skills limited to skills of members.

    c) Property limited to initial holdings of members and what is produced by them subsequently.

  3. Costs:

Building construction	$ 1,000,000
Tools and machinery	500,000
Land improvements, livestock	500,000
Furniture	200,000
Raw materials and six-month food supply	150,000
Initial labor expense, recruiting, public relations	300,000
Etc.	420,000
TOTAL	$ 3,070,000

And so on.

It is clear that Fourier's orientation was fundamentally that of a design engineer rather than that of a radical reformer. His free enterprise utopia was designed to maintain property rights, interest on capital, and existing inequalities in wealth. He addresses himself primarily to persons with investment capital at their disposal rather than to the unemployed or impoverished. His system offers the inducements of substantial financial returns to investors. His design is applied to production methods rather than to means of distribution. While applying the notion of complex division of labor to agricultural production, he retained his deep concern for the human participants in his system. He did not want them to suffer the degradation and boredom that accompanied this form of organization in the industrial settings he knew. It is perhaps in this sense that he can best be viewed as a humanist. It is clear, however, that his system could make sense only to the extent that it encountered virtually no unpredicted or strongly improbable situations.

II. *The Heuristic Approach.* The heuristic approach to system design is one that uses principles to provide guides for action. It is not bound by preconceptions about the situations the system will encounter. Its principles provide action guides even in the face of completely unanticipated situations and in situations for which no formal model or analytic solution is available.

The reader should be warned that this is not the currently legitimate dictionary connotation of the word "heuristic." The dictionary will tell you that heuristic is an adjective meaning to discover or to stimulate investigation. But it is really much more than a nondescript adjective (indeed we shall repeatedly use it as a noun as well as an adjective in the following pages). Its contemporary connotation in the data processing field is attributable to the efforts of Allen Newell, J. C. Shaw, and Herbert A. Simon, who call their truly creative innovations in computer-programming techniques "heuristic programming." These techniques are designed to facilitate higher order problem solving by computers in such areas as symbolic logic and chess.[5] Basic to these techniques is the use of operationally stated action principles providing directions to a computer faced with an unanalyzed or unanticipated situation.

Shortly after beginning work at the RAND Corporation in late 1953, I took part in some luncheon chess games. There existed among my lunch companions an interesting method for informally

---

[5] A. Newell and J. C. Shaw, "Programming the Logic Theory Machine," *Proceedings of the 1957 Western Joint Computer Conference* (February 1957); and A. Newell, J. C. Shaw, and H. A. Simon, "Chess Playing Programs and the Problem of Complexity," *IBM Journal of Research and Development,* II, No. 4 (October 1958), 320–335.

rating chess players. There were three-move players, four-move players, five-move players, and so on, depending upon how many moves one could "see ahead." "Seeing ahead" presumably meant exploring in detail every possibility that could arise in each possible network that could be generated as a result of a given move.

My companions had been steeped in the technology of computers and computer programming, which was then just developing. The efforts of such men as Shannon and Turing to program computers to play respectable games of chess had proceeded precisely along lines of exploring in detail the tributary networks of a given move (that is, if I do A, my opponent can do either 1, 2, 3, 4, or 5; if he does 1, I can do B, C, D, E, or F; if he does 2, I can do G, H, I, J, and so on). This approach did not work because of the tremendous number of possibilities that must be examined in limited time with computers possessing finite, if extremely large, memories.

This approach violated some fundamental notions I had about how to play chess effectively. For example, the chess books I was familiar with repeatedly talked about "principles" of good play—although none of them ever became very specific about how to use these principles in a specific, previously unencountered situation. One of the principles was called "development." I had never seen anyone get very specific about what "development" meant, but generally I understood it to mean something like, "get your pieces out into the open."

It finally occurred to me that when you moved a piece from one square to another, and discovered that there were more squares to which the piece could be moved afterward than there were before, the piece was considered to be developed. If you generalized this to a side of white or black pieces, you could say that one side was developed more than the opposing side if the total number of squares to which it could move its pieces was greater than the number for the opponent. If, at any given time, one wished to measure the relative development of either side, it was necessary merely to count the legal moves available to each side. A subsequent study of a chess tournament, which I made together with some colleagues, provided verification for the notion that development was indeed related to successful chess play.[6]

The point is that there was a different approach available, not only to chess strategy, but to computer programming as well —an approach made possible by the enunciation of working principles that could be operationally defined for computer-programming purposes. This is the method of heuristic programming developed by Newell, Simon, and Shaw. This team uses the term heuristic "to denote any principle or device that contributes to the reduction in the average search to solution."[7] This is necessary because the number of possible legal continuations five moves deep for each player in a game of chess, assuming an average of 25 legal possibilities at each stage, is about 10^{14} or one hundred million million.[8]

It is, of course, a trivial problem to program a high-speed computer to specify the best move in a chess game for a situation in which nothing appears on the chessboard but, for example, a white king, a black king, and a black rook. Moreover, there exist many other situations of a similar nature characteristically occurring toward the end of a game in which a more or less simple rule, procedure, or algorithm will provide an exact specification of what each side should do under every possible set of circumstances. The opening trap as well as the simple end game position in chess are clearly established situations for experienced players. It is the middle game of chess that best illustrates emergent situations. When the tributary networks of a given line of play cannot be explored in detail, it is possible to proceed by having available a principle of action (that is, a heuristic).

Among the classical utopians, the heuristic approach to system design is perhaps best illustrated by the work of Pierre-Joseph Proudhon. Proudhon did not prepare any blueprints for an

---

[6] Cf. R. Boguslaw, H. Garfinkel, W. J. Pelton, and M. A. Robinson, "Decision Making in Complex Situations: An Analysis of One Chess Tournament." Paper read at Annual Meeting of American Association for the Advancement of Science, 1958.

[7] A. Newell, H. Simon, and J. C. Shaw, "The Processes of Creative Thinking," p–1320 (Santa Monica, Calif.: The RAND Corporation, 1959).

[8] *Ibid.*, p. 20.

ideal society, yet he felt deeply that he understood the requirements for such a society. He simply employed a design technique
that someone like Fourier or other formalist designers would find
it difficult to appreciate. Fundamentally, this consisted of setting
forth general principles and insisting that the ideal society must
operate in consonance with these principles. It must do so whatever the specific nature of its operating structure happened to be.
This, of course, helps to explain why critics and historians have
always found it much easier to agree on what Proudhon was
against rather than to determine precisely what he was for. He
was not "for" any specific set of design specifications on any
specific tropic island. He was "for" his principles of liberty,
equality, fraternity, and above all, justice.

Undeniably Proudhon's principles were global and vague. A
serious-minded computer programmer would reject out-of-hand
any suggestion that his disordered heaps of verbiage could be
reduced to clear-cut specifications for behavior in concrete situations. But to characterize him simply as an anarchist (in the over-
simplified sense of an enemy of all government) is to do him and
his methodology a monumental injustice.

His utopia would, indeed, have describable content. The
nature of this content is simply different from that of other more
familiar varieties of utopia. It consists primarily of Proudhon's
vision of an all-encompassing action principle for human societies.
This principle he called "justice." In his own terms, "I build no
system . . . Justice, nothing else; that is the alpha and omega
of my argument; to others I leave the business of governing the
world. . . ."[9]

He shared with other classical utopians a profound conviction that the existing state of the world was lamentable. He
shared their conviction that it was necessary to find a more adequate set of social arrangements. But whereas the formalist
utopians attempted to provide a complete analysis of the range
of situations that their societies would encounter and tried to set
forth all design specification in meticulous detail, Proudhon was

---

[9] P. J. Proudhon, *What Is Property—An Inquiry into the Principle of
Right and of Government,* trans. Benjamin R. Tucker (New York: Hum-
boldt Publishing Company, n.d.), p. 14.

quite prepared to begin with the status quo. He severely criticized existing unsatisfactory institutional arrangements such as those relating to interest on capital, rent on land, and entrepreneurial profit. But the counterpart of this criticism was an implicit readiness to accept an infinite variety of alternate proposals—so long as they met the test of his action principles. A variety of structural arrangements within his utopia were possible if it could be demonstrated that no violence was done to these principles or heuristics.

III. *The Operating Unit Approach.* The operating unit approach begins neither with models of the system nor with selected principles. It begins with people or machines carefully selected or tooled to possess certain performance characteristics. The system or organization or utopia that ultimately unfolds will incorporate solutions that these units provide.

It is obvious that the various systems that get developed through the use of this approach are, to a considerable extent, based upon the range of flexibility possessed by the operating units. It is becoming increasingly apparent that flexibility in this sense is much more than a simple distinction between man and machine. Man may be inflexible, machines may be flexible—or vice versa. Under some conditions, it may be highly desirable to limit the range of operating unit flexibility to insure reliability and predictability of system performance. Under other conditions, the reverse may be true.

Thus, in B. F. Skinner's fictional utopia, called *Walden Two*,[10] it is clear that the flexibility of the human operating units is drastically limited to suit the requirements of the system as seen by its designer, an experimental psychologist named Frazier. The behavior of these units (people) is highly reliable, although no one has attempted to specify the situations in which they are to perform. One might almost postulate an infinity of possible system designs that might in fact emerge, and conceivably an infinity of principles or heuristics to which these systems could be required to adhere. Reliability in performance is achieved through conditioning the components to behave in a "reasonable" fashion.

---

[10] Cf. B. F. Skinner, *Walden Two* (New York: The Macmillan Company, 1948).

Walden Two has been called an "ignoble utopia," because it urges men to be something less than human.[11] "Human" in this context apparently refers to the properties of free choice or the wide range of possible responses that hopefully characterizes the unconditioned human being. It is perhaps a significant commentary on contemporary psychological and social science that its efforts often appear directed toward making men less than human through the perfecting of behavioral control techniques, while contemporary physical science seems to be moving in the direction of increasing the number of possible machine responses to environmental stimuli.

There exists a striking similarity between the use of human operating units in the *Walden Two* system and the use of physical equipment employed in contemporary system engineering. Goode and Machol, in their text on system engineering,[12] categorize the equipment used in systems into six classes. These include:

A. *Input Equipments:* These receive or accept the information or material inputs to the system. Included are such things as special-purpose automatic devices for standardizing inputs, for example, pressure devices for counting automotive vehicles, and mechanical feelers used in automatic checking systems for banks.

B. *Communication Equipments:* Depending upon whether the form of the message is voice, visual image, or code, these may consist of telegraph, television, radio, and so forth.

C. *Logical Control Equipments:* These are fundamentally digital or analogue computers that control the flow of information, process existing information to derive new information, and, if necessary, control the flow of material within the system.

D. *Reflexive Control Equipments:* These are essentially servo-mechanisms that consist of an error-detecting device, a de-

---

[11] Cf. R. L. Heilbroner, *The Worldly Philosophers* (New York: Simon & Schuster, Inc., 1953).

[12] Harry H. Goode and Robert E. Machol, *System Engineering, An Introduction to the Design of Large-Scale Systems* (New York: McGraw-Hill Book Company, 1957).

vice for amplifying this error, a power course, and some type of input- and output-actuating mechanism.

E. *Handling Equipments:* These are used to move material about in a system. If it is propulsion for airborne vehicles in which you are interested, four basic types are available: piston-propeller, turbojet, ram-jet, and rocket. In this order, they are increasingly less efficient and more powerful. It is clear that each type and each combination of these basic types possess enduring or at least reliable characteristics as an operating unit. It is also clear that, if one wishes to travel at Mach 3 (three times as fast as sound), one selects rockets rather than any of the other types of propulsion. If the system designer decides to use ram-jet, turbojet, or piston-propeller type of propulsion, his system may travel—but at a pace something less than Mach 3.

F. *Output Equipments:* These include effectors that carry out final system action vis-à-vis materials of various kinds and displays that provide information as an output.

If one persists in drawing gross comparisons between these equipments and the human operating units of *Walden Two,* certain strong similarities immediately become apparent. Input equipments may, of course, be compared with the sensory equipment of human beings—eyes, ears, nose, and so forth. Communication equipments take their place alongside of gestures, speech, and the more rudimentary forms of written communication among operating unit components. If we skip, for a moment, to handling equipments, the similarity of footpower or armpower becomes apparent, while output equipment is provided in the form of hands for effectors, and discriminators—auditory, oral, or visual—for displays. When we consider reflexive-control equipments, or servomechanisms, we discover it is here that the most extravagant claims have been made on behalf of hardware. Indeed, this is where some of the most notable developments have taken place in recent years. The basic problem involved, of course, is that of controlling something physical so that it obeys a given command. The physical something may be simply position, speed, or acceleration in a mechanical system; or it may involve such conditions as temperature, voltage, or neutron flux in other systems.[13]

In *Walden Two*, the problem of controlling the component operating units was accomplished through the behavioral engineering technique of psychological conditioning. As Frazier explains it, a code of conduct had been worked out that would presumably keep things running smoothly if everyone concerned behaved according to plan. It was recognized that to anticipate all future situations would be an impossible task. The planners, therefore, relied upon "self-control" that permitted each individual to act essentially as a servomechanism obeying commands generated within the code of conduct.

The problem that contemporary system engineers have solved no better than the designers of *Walden Two* is that of how to build a mechanism for generating an ever appropriate code of conduct. Such a mechanism must be able to size up its environment, decide upon some universally acceptable values, and accomplish all this without doing violence to the structure of its operating units. Engineers understand very well what it means to overload an electrical circuit or to place an excessive strain upon a mechanical assembly. Where these operating units are human, the evidence of strain, load, or deterioration may not be quite so apparent.

Gardner Murphy, whose primary concern is human beings, reminds us that most of our traditional utopias forget that men do not stay put. "A utopia which would fit the men of today," he tells us, "would be insipid or become a straightjacket to the men of tomorrow."[14] For one thing, the sheer specifications of these human equipments change. People produce people who produce people ad infinitum. But the people thus produced are by no means carbon copies of their predecessors. They vary in size, weight, memory, capacity, access time to memory, ability to manipulate the contents of memory, and in many other similar ways. Furthermore, they may be affected in unpredicted ways

---

[13] *Ibid.*, p. 456.

[14] Gardner Murphy, *Human Potentialities* (New York: Basic Books, Inc., 1958), p. 309.

by new experiences or fresh sensations. As a human operating unit wears out, one searches in vain through the parts catalogue for an exact replacement.

The operating unit approach, it is clear, can indeed provide some solutions to the problem of system design for emergent situations. But a fundamental contradiction remains—the historical dilemma between freedom and control. To the extent that we increase predictability and performance reliability by selecting predictable and reliable components, to that extent we reduce the system's freedom and its capacity to deal with emergent situations effectively. In this sense, reliable components reduce over-all system effectiveness. As we proceed in the other direction—that is, in the direction of building a system with self-sufficient operating units—we reduce the effectiveness of our control mechanism. This design problem poses the basic dilemma of freedom versus control. We shall keep exploring this dilemma throughout the remainder of our discussion.

IV. *The Ad Hoc Approach.* The ad hoc approach involves no commitment to models, principles, or operating units. It proceeds with a view of present reality as the only constant in its equation. The design process characteristically begins with a review of an existing system or state of affairs. Its subsequent course is, at every stage, a function of the then existing situation. The conceptual state of this approach is by far the least developed of all. It is used under several different conditions and for several different purposes.

It is frequently adopted when a future system is more or less clearly perceived by the system designer and the problem is one of implementation. Under these circumstances the ad hoc approach is used as a means of moving from the current state of affairs to the desired system state. Here the approach involves the use of many small changes seen as increments that will ultimately result in a completed system. The purpose of the approach under these conditions may include:

1. Providing an interim system until such time as the state of technology has improved sufficiently to permit a significantly different design.

2. Helping to change the climate of necessary attitudes as a preliminary to final system implementation.
3. Utilizing human or material resources as they become available.

The ad hoc approach may also be used when the designer has *no* clearly perceived view of the future system. Under these circumstances, attention may be focused on a group that is normally perceived as being external to the design process itself. Such a group may be referred to by such various descriptors as the "user," the "public," or the "customer." Here, the design process consists of ongoing determinations of the manifest or latent wishes of this group, and of designing a system to meet these needs. If the needs change, it is imperative that the system design be changed. The validation of design effectiveness is the extent to which these needs are seen as having been met.

The purpose of the approach under these conditions may be stated simply as an attempt to keep the customer (or user or public) happy. The advantages accompanying this purpose may range from the obvious one of increasing the probability of a continuous flow of resources, to the more subtle one of designing a system that will do the job it is intended to do rather than the job an enthusiastic engineer would wish it to do. The most obvious disadvantage inherent in the approach is the reliance it tends to place upon contemporary concepts and technology. This can easily result in a stifling of innovative efforts in these areas.

A third use of the ad hoc approach is found when neither the designer nor the user group has a clearly perceived view of the future system or even of its requirements. The salient feature of this state of affairs is the existence of a problem for which no solution currently exists. The system design efforts here are patterned after the Darwinian description of evolution. The problem is handled in any fashion that results in survival, and the configuration remaining in existence is the one viewed as a successful adaptation to environmental requirements. "Muddling through," a seat-of-the-pants technique, or simply "being practical" are popular descriptors for this use of the ad hoc approach to system design. The purpose of the approach under these conditions may be described as a *search* for a solution that is not currently available. Difficulties arising in connection with it include:

1. The relative absence of predictability.
2. The tendency to regard environmental conditions as fixed. This suggests adaptation within the system as the only design solution, and ignores the possibility of environment modification; for example, "But that is what the customer wants," or "That's all the public will stand for," and so forth.
3. The tendency to perpetuate temporary arrangements beyond their period of usefulness simply because they were at one time perceived as being part of the conditions sufficient, if not uniquely necessary, for success.

David E. Lilienthal's account of the Tennessee Valley Authority provides an interesting example of the ad hoc approach to system design. Lilienthal reports that visitors to the TVA frequently asked to see a copy of the TVA plan and looked in vain for a Department of Planning on the organization chart. Neither of these existed. Lilienthal maintains that in a democracy, plans must be based upon "here and now" and "things as they are." He insists that the people must be in on the planning and that their existing institutions must be made part of it. He recalls the story of the man who was asked by a stranger how to get to Jonesville. The punch line, "If I were you I wouldn't start from here," is used to characterize planning that does not begin with the current state of affairs.[15]

Some Social Implications of the Utopian Renaissance

In subsequent chapters we shall explore the contemporary faces of each of the four approaches to system design. We shall examine both their methodological adequacy and the implications they hold for those who are not designers. They embody the basic design techniques employed in the utopian renaissance

---

[15] David Lilienthal, *TVA—Democracy on the March* (New York: Harper & Row, Publishers, Inc., 1953).

and define the characteristic forms to which new applications of "automation" or "cybernation" will be shaped. They have profound implications both for the structure of contemporary societies and for the people who will continue to live within these societies.

Current assessments of the probable effects of automation or cybernation range from elaborately mild understatements to predictions of social and economic catastrophe. Indeed, at least one responsible economist[16] seriously suggests that current trends will shortly result in a shattering collapse of our present socioeconomic system. This system is geared to scarcity. People are given jobs to help reduce the scarcity by making goods or providing services. But, as scarcity is eliminated, with the aid of fewer and fewer people, we are faced with the prospect of permanent unemployment for a substantial segment of our former work force.

This is a far cry from the hope expressed in 1956 by sociologist Arnold Rose that the incipient automation revolution might lead, not to a Huxleyan world of mechanical monstrousness, but rather to a world of happier and more vital people. Such a world could be assured, Rose felt, through the use of "planning, foresight and a modicum of intelligent action on the part of the public and private organizations. . . ."[17]

But the automation revolution has *not* led to a world of happier and more vital people. Why not? Is it because of a lack of planning?

Planning *is* being done. It is being done by the manufacturers of computer hardware. It is being done (albeit unwittingly) by coders and computer programmers who specify the detailed procedures through which industrial tasks will be accomplished. It is being done by hardware engineers and operations research mathematicians who are the architects of our latter-day utopias. This, of course, is by no means a bad thing itself. But our latter-day dreamers repeat the technical errors of utopians throughout

---

[16] Cf. Robert Theobald, *Free Men and Free Markets* (New York: Clarkson N. Potter, Inc., 1963), p. 20.

[17] Arnold Rose, "Automation and the Future Society," *Commentary*, XXI, No. 3 (March 1956), 280.

the ages. In addition, not only have they lost the humanistic orientation that motivated so many of the classical utopian efforts, but also they proceed from a philosophical base in which traditional values of Western societies seem to be self-consciously excluded. Indeed, one of the most important social consequences of the utopian renaissance is the change it seems to be fostering in the traditional value-structure of Western people. For example, fundamental to Max Weber's Protestant Ethic is the notion that hard labor—sweat-of-the-brow-type labor—is essentially a good and desirable thing. But one of the proclaimed reasons for the utopian renaissance and its new technology is the abolition of hard labor. The workaday new utopians seem to have implicitly turned Max Weber's Ethic on its head to read, "Hard work is simply a temporarily unautomated task. It is a necessary evil until we get a piece of gear, or a computer large enough, or a program checked out well enough to do the job economically. Until then, you working stiffs can hang around—but, for the long run, we really don't either want you or need you."

Depending upon one's religious orientation, this reversal may be viewed as either a good or bad thing in itself. Its potential implications for persons who continue to live in an economic situation whose traditional values are being overturned are, in any event, enormous.

Science and engineering work has become glamorized in science fiction, the public press, TV, and motion pictures. The persons who engage in this kind of work are seen as having mysterious powers denied to the average man. Large portions of the worker and student population inevitably feel alienated—excluded from the possibility of participating in the new order. One might well predict that the identification of students, of members of the labor force, and indeed of the general population, will increasingly be with either the managerial or "scientific" classes of Western society. And for persons who feel they lack the educational or intellectual prerequisites to participate in scientific enterprises, the only available solution may be to identify exclusively with "management." The proliferation of management development programs in universities and industrial establishments, and increased popular participation in stock ownership, real estate speculation, and "white collar" crime, all may well be examined from this perspective. In the face of predictions regarding the disappearance of "middle management" as a functional requirement in advanced stages of industrial automation, the dilemmas confronting alienated would-be managers threaten to become even more anxiety provoking.

Here one may speculate regarding the successor to the Protestant Ethic. Will the unspoken creed, which once could be verbalized as "I may not be a brain but I can always make a living with these hands; I am fundamentally the producer," be replaced by another, which when verbalized might say, "All these hands (or all this mind) can do is what some machine hasn't yet gotten around to doing. The real producers in our society are the scientists, the engineers, and maybe even the boss. I am not *really* a producer—I feel alienated from the productive process. I am the one who's asking the others for a free ride. I am the one who, in effect, is doing the exploiting—why not do it deliberately and systematically?"

Many segments of society can be characterized by what has been called the "powerlessness" form of alienation—"the expectancy or probability held by the individual that his own behavior cannot determine the occurrence of the outcomes, or reinforcements, he seeks."[18] The notion that those strange men who write equations on blackboards are the real arbiters of all our destinies is one that must be obliterated in any society that wishes to continue functioning in even an approximately democratic fashion.

Other segments are subject to the kind of alienation called "isolation." This results from assigning low reward value to goals or beliefs that are typically high-valued in a given society.[19] Included among the groups affected are unquestionably some social scientists, some philosophers, and possibly some former bomber pilots. Funds for research on missile fuels are demonstrably more available than, say, funds for research in basic social theory, or philosophical theory, or manned bomber tactics. For some bomber pilots this may result in irrational and intem-

[18] M. Seeman, "On the Meaning of Alienation," *American Sociological Review*, XXIV (December 1959), 784.

[19] *Ibid.*, 789.

perate attacks upon the effectiveness of missiles. The rebellion of social scientists and philosophers against this imbalance in value structures can, and frequently does, take the form of avoiding professional involvement with some of the most centrally significant social issues in the contemporary world.

One implication of all this seems clear. In terms of sheer self-survival, it is necessary to expand the educational base of leaders and rank-and-file members of union and management organizations, military men, philosophers, social scientists, and others through broad educational programs. Such programs should be addressed not only to the problem of making people more at ease with the concept of computers and computer programming, but also more fundamentally toward helping them become perceptive about the implications that contemporary large-scale system design has for each one of us. This should permit union leaders, social scientists, academicians, management, and government officials, as well as an informed public, to participate along with more hardware-oriented engineers in the design of large-scale systems at an early stage of formulation of these projects. This must be done to insure that the human implications of proposed automated systems are fully explored as fundamental design variables.

In turn, physical scientists and engineers must become increasingly more sensitive to the human purposes that improvements in automated technology will serve. They must broaden the educational base of their training so that they do indeed consider *all* significant variables in designing systems—rather than merely those that lend themselves to hardware implementation or formal modeling. For example, significant design variables that should be included in any large-scale design effort include:

1. Retraining costs for displaced workers.
2. The costs for training students not only in existing skills but for jobs that are nonexistent at the time they are being educated.
3. Costs involved in dislocation of communities. Some of these —such as housing, transportation, public services, and the like—are susceptible of direct measurement while others

can only be estimated within the limits of relatively large standard deviations.

4. Mental health costs—including:

   a. Difficulties arising from loss of status because job skills have been automated out of existence.

   b. Problems arising from dislocation—tearing people away from an established social and work environment.

   c. Problems arising from the fact that although job enlargement and rotation may result in greater job interest and satisfaction, they also tend to create more tension for the individual.

   d. Tensions associated with the problem of unlearning old skills as well as the need to learn new ones.

It is hoped that in the following pages we can begin to explore some of the considerations that must accompany any intelligent attempt to incorporate such variables within the framework of the systems currently being designed under the impetus of the utopian renaissance.

2

SYSTEM IDEAS—
FOR WHOM AND FOR WHAT

One of the more interesting semantic anomalies of our
times is the varied esteem in which the word "system" is held.
Solar observatories and communication satellites are proudly
discussed by manufacturers and engineers as part of enormous
space systems; ballistic missiles and nuclear bombs constitute
large-scale missile systems; electronic computers and detailed
policy statements are combined to form glossy management
systems. These and many other comparable configurations are
systems held in exceptionally high esteem these days. But philosophical systems, social systems, political systems, and economic
systems seem to constitute a different species. These latter systems do not shine in the reflected glory of our new technology,
and their very mention is apt to make the well-adjusted American
somewhat uncomfortable. To information-processing specialists,
corporation managers, engineers, and military experts, using the
word system is to be *au courant* about the latest in technical
fashion and good taste. To economists, public officials, and de-
bating societies of all varieties, the same word is likely to connote
loss of individual freedom, right-wing totalitarianism, or simply
thunder on the left.

One thing seems clear. The word system is used by different people to communicate different ideas. Let us see what some of those ideas are.

THE CONNECTIVE IDEA

The most obvious examples of the connective idea in relation to systems are found in simple mechanisms of physical objects. The idea is perhaps best conveyed by the lyrics of the once-popular song that describes how "the ankle bone [is] connected to the leg bone, the leg bone connected to the knee bone, the knee bone connected to the hip bone," etc. A system in these terms then becomes a matter of providing intermediate variations to what is essentially a single purpose. The old Rube Goldberg cartoon devices, which introduced extraordinary complexity into the achievement of a straightforward mechanical task, illustrate the classic means by which ingenuity can confound simple purpose. A. D. Hall and R. E. Fagen provide us with an example of this idea in their discussion of a "physical system." They begin with a spring, a mass, and a solid ceiling. Physically these components can be viewed as unrelated until someone decides to connect the mass to the spring. This creates a system. Specifically, the length of the spring, the distance of the mass from the ceiling, the spring tension, and the size of the mass are all related. Similarly, if we consider, for simplicity's sake, only the turntable and arm of a record player, the amplifier, the speaker, and the cabinet —we do not have a high fidelity sound machine. But with the help of electricity, these parts and their various attributes become related to each other and form part of a coherent system. This relationship has a characteristic form. At each of a series of successive stages, performance is dependent upon performance in other stages (for example, mechanical vibrations in the speaker are related to amplifier currents and voltages).[1]

---

[1] A. D. Hall and R. E. Fagen, "Definition of System," *General Systems Yearbook of the Society for the Advancement of General Systems Theory*, Vol. I, ed. Ludwig Von Bertalanffy and Anatol Rapoport (Ann Arbor, Mich.: Braun-Brunfield, Inc., 1956).

THE IDEA OF CONTROL

The idea of control consists essentially of the notion that the results of a given action must be consistent with some given set of values. In the field of engineering this idea is associated with "control systems," which are generally classified as either open-loop or closed-loop systems.

If you heat your room with a gas heater and the gas heater works with a manually operated on-off switch, you have an open-loop system. If you use a gas furnace that gets turned off and on with a thermostat, you have a closed-loop system.

The idea of control in relation to systems has been used in oil refineries and chemical plants to regulate temperatures, pressure levels, and flow rates. The more dramatic uses involve the replacement of people on jobs characterized as "low level" or "routine." The advantages of using physical control devices as compared with using human beings are obvious. The physical devices are much more rapid than their human competitors; they don't get tired, bored, or inattentive; they can be used in situations unhealthful or dangerous to human beings (unmanned spacecraft, for example); they don't join unions or professional societies. They possess all the glamour and promise of science fiction robots. They are the stuff of which science fiction automation is made.

The idea of control was implicit in Walter B. Cannon's original formulation of the concept homeostasis. Cannon observed[2] that for a short time men can be exposed to dry heat at 239° to 261° Fahrenheit without an increase of their body temperature above normal. Arctic mammals can be exposed to cold 31° below zero Fahrenheit without any significant drop in body temperature. Moreover, persons who live in regions where the air is extremely dry have little difficulty in retaining their body fluids. Cannon suggested that the methods used by higher animals

---

[2] Walter B. Cannon, *The Wisdom of the Body*, rev. ed. (New York: W. W. Norton & Company, Inc., 1939), p. 22.

to maintain their body processes at an even keel might contain some useful notions for establishing, regulating, and controlling steady states in other kinds of organizations—including social and industrial organizations, which are notorious for their ups and downs. It was the body's ability to maintain its equilibrium that Cannon referred to as homeostasis. He then proceeded to speculate that comparative study might show that "every complex organization must have more or less effective self-righting adjustments in order to prevent a check on its functions or a rapid disintegration of its parts when subject to stress."[3]

It was a colleague of Cannon, Arthur Rosenblueth, who worked closely with Norbert Wiener and helped formulate the original statement of *cybernetics*. This term was introduced by Wiener in 1948 to refer to "the entire field of control and communication theory, whether in the machine or in the animal."[4]

In communication theory the idea of closed system is conveyed by the term "feedback," which has reference to what happens when the output of an electrical circuit is used as a portion of the input to the same circuit.

Wiener explained, in the following terms, his own rationale for linking communication and control in his definition of cybernetics: "When I control the actions of another person, I communicate a message to him, and although this message is in the imperative mood, the technique of communication does not differ from that of a message of fact. Furthermore, if my control is to be effective I must take cognizance of any messages from him which may indicate that the order is understood and has been obeyed."[5]

He went on to observe that giving an order to a machine was not fundamentally different from giving an order to a person. From the point of view of the person giving the order, the significant fact is that the order has gone out and a signal of compliance has returned. The fact that the signal has proceeded through a

---

[3] *Ibid.*, p. 25.
[4] Norbert Wiener, *Cybernetics* (New York: John Wiley & Sons, Inc., 1948), p. 19.
[5] Norbert Wiener, *The Human Use of Human Beings* (New York: Doubleday & Company, Inc., 1954), p. 16.

machine rather than a person is irrelevant. "Thus the theory of control in engineering, whether human or animal or mechanical, is a chapter in the theory of messages."[6]

If one wishes to adhere to this engineering frame of reference, it is possible to think of human beings as materials with more or less specifiable performance characteristics. Assuming that you have an order to give, and that part of your circuit includes people, it becomes necessary to understand the amount of work that can be accomplished by these people components, the time necessary to accomplish the work, the reliability of performance, the maintenance schedule required, and so on.

The customary consequence of adhering to this frame of reference is to conclude that human components are exasperatingly unreliable, limited, and inefficient. Furthermore, they are very difficult to control. The most obvious analogy to the physical control system involves the use of formal authority and its delegation as the energy or power source necessary to insure that the desired signals pass through the entire system. This, of course, is the basis for the insistence upon unquestioning obedience to orders traditionally found not only in military organizations but in all bureaucracies of both private industry and government organizations. Human groups unfortunately (or fortunately) have devised many mechanisms for disrupting systems that exercise control exclusively or even primarily through the use of authority.

What happens when authority control systems run amuck is an endless source of case history material for management development seminars. The case of the employees who do *everything* they are ordered to do by their supervisor—neither more nor less —is a classic. They ignore obvious emergent situations and engage in assigned repetitive tasks beyond reasonable termination points. The supervisor is gradually forced into behavior indistinguishable from that of a computer programmer giving instructions to a stupid but completely obedient machine. The case of the industrial work group ordered to use a new, unwanted piece of equipment is perennially effective slapstick comedy material; the

---

[6] *Ibid.*, pp. 16–17.

ingenious steps taken by members of the group to prove the existence of unsuspected faults in the new equipment provide universally understandable material for comedy writers. The list of examples could be continued indefinitely. The point to be made is simply this: The idea of control results in highly unreliable performance when applied to human components of a system.

The Interdisciplinary Idea

The leading exponent of this idea is Ludwig Von Bertalanffy who has led the contemporary search for a "general system theory."

Bertalanffy points to the increasing requirements in modern science for specialization—which results from the amount of available data, and the complexity of techniques and theoretical structures in every field. "The physicist, the biologist, the psychologist and the social scientist are, so to speak, encapsulated in a private universe, and it is difficult to get word from one cocoon to another."[7] When word does manage to get from one cocoon to another, we find the emergence of disciplines like cybernetics and information theory. But an acute observer may note that these disciplines quickly build their own cocoons and, in the process of so doing, erect unprecedented barriers to inter-cocoon communication.

An intriguing aspect of the interdisciplinary idea has been described by E. H. Porter, who makes his point by means of a "parable."[8]

The parable tells of the president of a large chain of short-order restaurants who hired a team of consultants to help him solve some human relations problems within his organization. Each consultant provided him with a reasonable analysis and solution—but while each analysis was different all *solutions* were identical.

---

[7] Ludwig Von Bertalanffy, "General System Theory," *Yearbook* (February 1956), 1.

[8] Cf. E. H. Porter, "The Parable of the Spindle," *Harvard Business Review* (May–June 1962), 58–66.

The sociologist observed that the human relations difficulties occurred during rush hours and were grounded in status problems. Waitresses, whose status was lower than that of the cooks, were required to give orders to the cook. This could be remedied by using a "spindle" on the order counter. The waitresses then could give orders to an impersonal spindle rather than to a cook, and the problem could be solved.

The psychologist (presumably possessing a Freudian bias) saw the manager in the father role, the cook in the son role, and the waitress in the daughter role. Allowing the daughter to issue orders to the son causes ego problems. Solution? The spindle.

The anthropologist analyzed the problem in terms of value conflict and also proposed the spindle solution.

Porter analyzes the system functions served by the spindle and discusses a "system" frame of reference. Within this frame, organizations are viewed as systems that transform information from one form to another. Their specific concern is the problem of handling various conditions of information overload.

In retrospect it appears that Porter has pointed up the difficulties arising when a social science framework is applied to problems more appropriately handled through the use of a model borrowed from classical physics. His parable rests upon several implicit assumptions. Probably the most important of these is the one that says that the tasks to be performed by the waitresses and cook are sufficiently stable; the environment sufficiently predictable; and the technology for accomplishing these tasks sufficiently well-known—so that a physical device (the spindle) can be made to deal with the necessary information-processing task in a satisfactory fashion. Under these circumstances, the analyses of the various consultants are useful only to the extent that they help throw some light on the motivational patterns of the various members of the restaurant team. The recommendations they make do not stem from an analysis of the functions of the restaurant but from an analysis of the needs of the human participants in the restaurant system.

To extend Porter's paradigm somewhat, one might raise a question about the fundamental requirement for waitresses or cooks. With the use of comparatively little ingenuity, one might construct an automatic signaling and conveyor device for ordering and delivering the food to customers at their respective tables. Before hastily embarking upon such a program, the wise restaurateur would do well to assess the extent to which waitresses meet customer needs that are over and above their information-processing and conveyor functions. In short, what reference frames are, after all, the most utilitarian in this situation?

THE BIG PICTURE IDEA

Suppose you are the manager of a baseball team. Your job is to organize a team that will win baseball games. To win a baseball game your team must score more runs than its opponents. If it does this, it wins the game. Winning a game is the criterion of effective team performance.

But what is the criterion for effective performance in the case of an individual player—say, the shortstop?

A shortstop may field or hit. Let us consider the fielding function. It is possible to divide the baseball field into segments and divide fielding responsibilities among the nine players. The criterion for effective individual fielding performance by the shortstop would then be the percentage of balls hit into his area of responsibility that he fielded without "error." This is demonstrably inefficient as a criterion for effective shortstop performance. The baseball field is too large to permit nine players to police every square inch with equal effectiveness. Consequently, if the batter is left-handed, the fielders may "swing to the right"; if the batter is known to be a good hitter, the fielders may "play him deep." When the pitcher can be depended on to throw the ball over the outside corner of home plate, the fielders can reasonably predict that the ball, if hit, will not be "pulled," and so on. For every batter, and indeed, for every pitch, the optimal distribution of fielding responsibility may be required to shift. Moreover, the areas of responsibility on a baseball field can only be drawn with imaginary lines. The ability of any given fielder to perceive instantly whether a specific ball will enter his current area of responsibility or the area of an adjoining fielder is limited.

Misperceptions will predictably occur with great frequency. A fielder who feels no responsibility for balls outside his area of responsibility could well contribute to the downfall of his own team while playing in an "errorless" fashion.

Effective baseball players are not, of course, rigid about responsibility allocation. To avoid collisions and situations where the ball may fall between two fielders, effective team players use such devices as "calling" for a given ball. This amounts to an assumption of responsibility on the part of the person doing the calling. An effective team player may risk incurring an individual error while attempting to field a ball that clearly has been hit into the area of responsibility of an adjoining fielder.

The batting function can superficially be analyzed as a matter of getting more and better hits. "Better" here would presumably consist of a linear progression: A two-base hit is better than a one-base hit, a three-base hit is better than a two-base hit, and so forth. Of course, any hit is better than no hit.

Based on this analysis, one might establish performance criteria for individual batters exclusively in terms of hits. The task for an individual batter as he approaches the plate would then be to get a hit. But this, of course, is scarcely consistent with the team objective of winning the game. When another member of the team has reached first base it may well be that optimal strategy would require self-immolation by the batter in the form of a sacrifice bunt, for example. Or, it may be that team strategy requires the batter to attempt to hit a ball he knows is badly pitched simply to protect his teammate on a "hit and run" play.

In short, as manager of the team, you must attempt to establish criteria for individual performance directly related to team requirements under all circumstances. You will find that baseball custom helps you in this effort. Thus, for example, in calculating the "batting average" of a given batter, "sacrifices" are typically not counted as turns "at bat." Also, individual players are given informal approbation for the undefined quality of "hustle," which ultimately probably refers to their sense of team purpose.

In the design of large-scale systems, the sense of ultimate team purpose is characteristically much more difficult to record and evaluate than it is on the baseball field. System psychologist John L. Kennedy notes that one possible approach is through the specification of measurable subcriteria, which have many of the aggregative properties of, for example, cost in dollars.[9] In short, the problem becomes one of evaluating, in specific, quantitative form, all the things that go on within a system in terms of the ultimate system criterion. Since this itself is apt to be rather indistinct in the case of a large-scale system, difficulties exist at the very outset.

Beyond this, however, is a fact underlying much of Kennedy's discussion. As tasks and responsibilities are allocated within a system, the system criterion—the big-picture payoff, if you will—tends to be forgotten by elements of the system that now have "subsystem" or individual criteria with which to concern themselves. The big-picture idea in systems is addressed primarily to this situation and to efforts that will alleviate it.

One contemporary instrument based on the big-picture idea is SAIM—the Systems Analysis and Integration Model. As described by its inventors, Albert Shapero and Charles Bates, Jr., SAIM is a "descriptive matrix model that classifies the elements of a weapon system into those determining the nature and form of the system, those comprising the parts of the system, and those integrating the parts of the system."[10] It provides us with a classification of "system elements" for use in a variety of systems. The classification scheme itself is vaguely reminiscent of the old rhyme that goes,

> Big fleas have little fleas
> Upon their backs to bite 'em;
> Little fleas have lesser fleas
> And so ad infinitum.

Specifically, "Every system is a subsystem of some larger system

---

[9] John L. Kennedy, "Psychology and System Development," *Psychological Principles in System Development*, ed. Robert M. Gagne (New York: Holt, Rinehart & Winston, Inc., 1962), pp. 22–23.
[10] Albert Shapero and Charles Bates, Jr., *A Method for Performing Human Engineering Analysis of Weapon Systems* (WADC Technical Report 59–784, September 1959) (Wright Patterson Air Force Base, Ohio: Aerospace Medical Laboratory, Wright Air Development Center, Air Research and Development Command, USAF) p. 5.

and is itself made up of a hierarchy of subsystems, sub-subsystems, sub-sub-subsystems, etc., each of which is a system in its own right."[11]

At any given level of generality, the elements of a system under the SAIM scheme can be divided into:

1. Determinants: elements outside the operating system itself which determine the nature, form, and limits of the system. These include such items as general and specific statements of the system's purpose, inputs from other systems, and the constraints of all sorts which place bounds upon the system.
2. Components: the "moving parts" of the system, which include the mechanisms, men, and facilities within the system.
3. System Integrators: elements that integrate the moving parts. These include "operational sequences, communications, organization, and decision structure."[12]

The view of the system thus provided is one that defines the big picture as the view from the top of a pyramid. Only those bricks are acceptable which have a specific reason for being there. Carbuncles, nonstandard quality bricks, and the like, can be detected and eliminated.

Still another version of the big-picture idea is found in a technique widely used by industrial and government agencies to evaluate performance within an activity devoted to research and development activities. PERT (Program Evaluation and Review Technique) was originally devised for use with the United States Navy Polaris Fleet Ballistic Missile Program. It is used to provide a view of a research and development program as a "network of interrelated events to be achieved in proper ordered sequence. Basic data for the analysis consist of elapsed-time estimates for activities which connect dependent events in the network. The time estimates are obtained from responsible technical persons and are subsequently expressed in probability terms."[13]

[11] *Ibid.*, p. 6.
[12] *Ibid.*, p. 8.
[13] D. G. Malcolm, *et al.*, "Application of a Technique for R&D Program Evaluation," *SP-62* (Santa Monica, Calif.: System Development Corporation, March 30, 1959), p. 1.

The philosophy underlying this technique adheres to traditional military concepts of order and control. Specifically, this philosophy insists that the purpose of controls and management control systems is to provide directions for establishing concrete goals and measuring progress made toward these goals. To achieve such control, it is necessary to organize, plan, schedule, and establish controls for inventories, quality, cost, and manpower.[14]

In PERT itself, all information required is coded for use in a computer program. The computer then calculates the expected completion time for each system event, the location of slack and critical areas in the research and development program, the probability of equaling or meeting the current schedule, and the latest date by which every event must be completed to meet the specified deadlines.[15]

THE ORGANISM IDEA

If a system is a "thing," what kind of a thing is it like? Herbert Spencer asked himself this question late in the nineteenth century. The system he was concerned with was society or the social system. He observed that a mass that has disintegrated into fragments ceases to be a thing. Similarly, stones, bricks, and wood become a thing called a house if they are arranged in some definite way. "It is the permanence of the relations among component parts which constitutes the individuality of a whole as distinguished from the individualities of its parts."[16]

In answering his question, Spencer decided that there were two "classes of aggregates" with which the social system could be compared: the inorganic and the organic. He promptly dismissed the possibility that it could be compared with the inorganic since "a whole of which the parts are alive cannot, in its general

---

[14] Cf. *ibid.*, pp. 1–2.
[15] *Ibid.*, p. 36.
[16] Herbert Spencer, *The Principles of Sociology*, 3rd ed. (New York: Appleton-Century-Crofts, 1904), I, 447–448.

characters, be like lifeless wholes."[17] He then discussed several reasons for comparing it with a living body.

In the first place, societies, like biological organisms, exhibit "augmentation of mass," that is, they grow. Some inorganic things such as crystals also grow, but this growth is significantly different from growth in societies and living bodies. Moreover, both societies and living bodies become more complex in structure as they grow. A third similarity, regarded by Spencer as highly important, is that in both society and living organisms there exists a "mutual dependence of parts," for example, stopping the motion of the lungs causes a stoppage of the heart; loss of one eye deprives the body of a service essential to its preservation; in a society, the clothiers cannot carry on their business without those who spin and weave textile fabrics, and so on. Finally, the lives of both society and living organisms are different from the lives of their component units. In both cases, the life of the system lasts longer than the lives of the units; however, it is also possible for the system to be destroyed without destroying the lives of its component units.[18]

It is, of course, easy to get carried away by facile analogies between societies and biological organisms. Howard Becker and Harry Elmer Barnes have summarized the analogies of this sort used by social theorists beginning with the efforts of the ancient Greeks, Romans, and Hindus.[19] They conclude that to persist in the analogy does not make sound scientific sense.

But, rejecting the physical *organism* analogy does not mean that the term *organic* cannot be retained as a useful construct. Many years ago, L. T. Hobhouse explained it all in the following terms: ". . . the life of society and the life of an individual do resemble each other in certain respects, and the term 'organic' is as justly applicable to one as to the other. For an organism is a whole consisting of interdependent parts. Each part lives and functions and grows by subserving the life of the whole. It

---

[17] *Ibid.*, p. 448.

[18] *Ibid.*, pp. 452–455.

[19] Cf. Howard Becker and Harry Elmer Barnes, *Social Thought from Lore to Science,* 2nd ed. (Washington, D.C.: Harren Press, 1962), p. 677. the analogy does not make sound scientific sense.

sustains the rest and is sustained by them, and through their mutual support comes a common development. . . ."[20]

And John L. Kennedy has recently revived the previously discarded organismic framework as an aid in the conceptualization of contemporary large-scale man-machine systems. He describes systems as "synthetic" organisms with functions analogous to those of biological organisms and a life cycle with stages such as birth (operational environment test), infancy (initial operational capability), maturity (full operation with other systems), and senescence (phasing out for obsolescence).[21] This framework helps provide him with a practical method for analyzing the interventions made by system developers and system managers. These interventions include such things as the selection of human beings for participation in the system, training them, and providing tools, machines, and work environments.[22] The framework also reinforces the notion that studying personnel problems or machine problems in isolation "begs the question of total system performance."[23]

In short, Kennedy, too, seems to be primarily concerned with the organic idea rather than the organismic analogy as a means for conceptualizing interrelatedness. But he goes beyond Hobhouse as well as Becker and Barnes in his concern for interrelatedness—not only with respect to human beings alone, but among human beings and their physical environment, their tools, and their machines.

This search for an all-encompassing contemporaneous interrelatedness is strongly reminiscent of Kurt Lewin's field theory. As Lewin explained it, field theory analysis proceeds, *not* by "picking out one or another isolated element within a situation, the importance of which cannot be judged without consideration of the situation as a whole," but rather by starting with a "characterization of the situation as a whole."[24]

---

[20] Leonard T. Hobhouse, *Social Evolution and Political Theory* (New York: Columbia University Press, 1922), p. 87.

[21] John L. Kennedy, *op. cit.*, p. 14.

[22] Cf. *ibid.*, p. 12.

[23] *Ibid.*, p. 23.

[24] Kurt Lewin, "Field Theory and Learning," *Field Theory in Social*

Thus, he asks us to consider the problem of studying a group consisting of five members during a given period of time. Assuming that five observers are available, two distinct methods of study are possible. The "natural" procedure would seem to consist of assigning one observer to each group member and gathering five biographies. An alternate (and more effective method) would consist of assigning the five observers to such tasks as observing the "subgrouping," recording the interactions that occur and the nature of these interactions. In short, it is not, as he puts it, that the whole is *more* than the sum of its parts; it is *different* from the sum of its parts.[25]

For Whom and For What

Ideas alone do not build systems; they are built by "practical" men. But practical men throughout the ages have tended to be suspicious of disembodied ideas and full-time dealers in ideas. These dealers may include representatives from many different occupations and devotees of a wide range of avocations. Their ranks may include philosophers, scientists, scholars, professors, teachers, or students. In short, they are the "longhairs."

Obviously this gulf between ideation and action is not insuperable. Ideas, like dreams, do on occasion become realized. But every society and every epoch has a special technique for facilitating the process. In our own contemporary world, this technique can be recognized by the use of a word—"applied." An applied scientist is a scientist who has had his hair cut. An applied science is a science without fuzzy edges.

"Applied" can be either a redundancy or an affectation. With respect to engineering or carpentry, for example, it is a redundancy; with respect to philosophy it may seem to be more of an affectation.

Science, ed. Dorwin Cartwright (New York: Harper & Row, Publishers, Inc., 1951), p. 63.
[25] Cf. *ibid.,* pp. 146–154.

Let us for a moment consider the carpenter.

A carpenter may saw, hammer, drill, plane, or measure; he may be working on a building frame, shelf, bookcase, door, or fence. He may be employed by a large industrial firm, a government agency, or a small building contractor; or he may serve as his own entrepreneur or engage in carpentry as a hobby. But ordinarily we do not feel that this heterogeneity of activity and purposes is especially confusing—we think we can encompass the job of a carpenter by stating a frame of reference, namely, wood.

But wood, of course, is scarcely sufficient—even as a frame of reference. It does not serve to distinguish the carpenter from the organic chemist, the botanist, or the cabinet maker.

Our notions about what carpenters do are derived from our observations of what in fact they have done and what they say they can do. For example, we find something appropriate as well as something ridiculous about the child who, after driving a nail into the floor with a hammer, announces: "Look Ma, I'm a carpenter."

Carpentry, teaching, engineering, medicine, and law all involve "doing something." The "doing" consists of action taken in specific situations ("practicing" medicine, "practicing" law, and so forth). With respect to some situations, the action to be taken is perfectly predictable and perhaps even specified in a handbook. These, of course, are the situations we have called established. In emergent situations, however, we must apparently place complete reliance upon the skill or "intuition" of the person taking the action.

A repairman replacing a tube in a TV set has either encountered an identical situation previously or can refer to a book that, in effect, describes more or less precisely the situation in which he finds himself. Moreover, the book indicates in explicit terms the specific and detailed actions he must take to deal effectively with this situation. A teacher, on the other hand, confronted with an inattentive or unruly class does not usually have such a book. He must rely upon "skill" or "intuition." But the fact that there exist experienced and effective teachers does not mean that we have direct access to the technology or art which contributes to this effectiveness or that we can readily communicate this technology or art to the student teacher.

This, then, is one of the fundamental problems of application: On the one hand, the temptation is almost overpowering to establish the techniques and practices of practitioners as handbook truths available in situations of the sort we have termed established. It is the temptation to speak with the same degree of assurance under all professional circumstances as does the familiar stereotype of a TV repairman or a journeyman carpenter.

On the other hand, there may be found equally strong temptations to revert to unbridled intuitionism—on the part of those who somehow sense the inadequacy of established situation science applied to emergent situation reality.

The problem exists wherever we find practitioners who must act in the face of emergent situations. It takes the form of dividing scientists as well as ordinary people into two more or less armed camps—the "truth seekers" on the one hand and the "significance seekers" on the other. The former take the view that one cannot proceed to "apply" except where the indisputable sanction of scientific experiment has established an incontrovertible truth. The truths thus established, however, may appear to refer to "unreal" or "trivial" situations. "Truth" is achieved by confining one's efforts to the definitive analysis of established situations. Since these are frequently not the situations that most concern either the professional practitioner or the practical man, the findings frequently cannot be applied in a direct fashion.

The "significance seekers," on the other hand, may offer a multiplicity of explanations in the form of "guesses," hunches, or even "theories" to justify action in a socially significant situation. Upon careful examination, however, it is often found that such explanations are expressed in terms sufficiently vague and non-operational so that a variety of inconsistent actions might be justified in the name of the same explanation. For example, an "applied" businessman, subscribing to the "theory" that operating costs must be cut to the bone, can define a new office or a new Cadillac as being inside or outside the "bone" depending upon a large number of unstated factors. When pressed for an explanation the last defense of an experienced business practitioner might well be, "I am not bound by my theoretical formulations. I do what I think is best in the situation."

The applied scientist, or the system designer, however, usually feels obligated to say what course of action is better and why it is better—given the value premises under which he is operating.

This frequently poses the dilemma of decision making within the context of uncertain or even inconsistent criteria. In attempting to determine which course of action is "better" it is possible to consider short-run effects on the one hand and more remote long-run effects on the other. Is it better to give the crying child a piece of candy now, or should one focus on the tummyache that may develop in several hours? or perhaps upon the long-range personality effects upon the child of either gratification or denial?

It may be necessary to determine whether it is *good* for the child to stop crying and *bad* for him to have a tummyache. An ache may be bad for the tummy, but is it bad for the child as a whole? A stomach specialist and a psychiatrist conceivably could give quite different answers to these questions—while each of them is in the process of abiding by irreproachable professional or scientific standards. And so, the initial question, "What is better?" very rapidly can become transformed into the question, "For Whom and For What?"

In the following chapters we shall keep asking these questions, implicitly if not explicitly, as we examine in more detail the methods, techniques, and intellectual underpinnings of the various approaches to system design. What are the latent assumptions that shape the direction and form of our contemporary utopias? For whom are they made and for what purpose? What are the potential achievements and limitations of the twentieth-century efficiency ideologies that begin with electronic computers and end in ideational strait jackets? For whom do they represent achievements and for whom do they represent limitations? Who are the good guys? Who are the bad guys?

Or perhaps, one might rather wish to ask, what are *these* guys good for? What are *those* guys good for? For whom are they good? Why?

FORMALIST DESIGNS

One of the most vocal and controversial of mid-twentieth-century spokesmen for the formalist approach to system design is Herman Kahn, the former RAND Corporation scientist, whose book, *On Thermonuclear War*, evoked storms of protests from humanistic critics throughout the world. The burden of this criticism consists of charges that his handling of the problems of war and peace is "insensitive," "cruel," and "heartless." Kahn himself unquestionably regards his work as being simply intelligent. Let us see.

To begin with, it is important to observe that Kahn is not a naïve misanthrope who proceeds with a supreme disregard for human life and welfare. As a matter of fact, he is careful to explain his concept of good planning. It must consider not only narrowly defined military solutions but also such alternatives as arms controls, other methods for easing international tensions, and the possible desirability of reducing national budgets. Indeed, Kahn obviously takes considerable pride in the breadth of his approach as compared with the more traditional methods of analysis used at RAND. The old RAND method consisted of a search for an optimum system after some set of fundamental assumptions had been specified. The procedure involved the comparison of enormous numbers of different configurations and selecting the one demonstrably best—given the criteria and assumptions that had been specified. If you were going to engage in this kind of activity, it was helpful to have a high-speed computer around. But Kahn cannot resist the opportunity to poke fun at his former colleagues and their boasts about the number of calculations used in a given analysis.

All this is contrasted with Kahn's own viewpoint. This, he asserts, is different. Instead of comparing a large number of different systems under a relatively few sets of conditions, he undertakes to compare a small number of systems under a great many different conditions. In addition, he tries to avoid using only a single criterion of performance. He selects a system as satisfactory if it achieves high-priority objectives reasonably well, considers medium- or low-priority conditions in its analysis, and protects against some forms of improbable situation. The system selected is not necessarily the optimum one in terms of the high-priority objective, as was the case under the old RAND method.

The point to be made here, of course, is that both the old and the new viewpoints described by Kahn are variants of what we have called the formalist approach to system design. The controversy he has generated can probably best be explained by noting that his critics simply disagree with his judgments about what constitutes high- and low-priority objectives. But what about the formalist approach itself? What kinds of things can the approach accomplish? What kinds of things should it not be required to do?

We have defined the formalist approach as one involving the use of models. To the extent that this is seen as being confined to the use of symbolic models, and especially symbolic models of the "mathematical" variety, it would seem that the entire field of operations research, for example, is restricted to the use of the formalist approach. A standard text[1] in this field defines operations research as a scientific search for optimal solutions to problems

---

[1] C. West Churchman, Russell L. Ackoff, and E. Leonard Arnoff, *Introduction to Operations Research* (New York: John Wiley & Sons, Inc., 1957), p. 18.

involved in the operations of a system. Indeed, the text provides a handbook specification of the appropriate method for engaging in the operations research process. One begins by "formulating" the problem, and constructing a mathematical model of the system he wishes to study. One then derives a solution from the model. It now becomes simply a matter of technique to test the model and the solution derived from it. After setting up appropriate controls, one is ready to put the solution to work.

Let us briefly examine some of the favorite models of operations researchers.

THE LINEAR PROGRAMMING MODEL

The *Tableau Economique* that François Quesnay produced in 1758 has been described as a crude example of a linear programming model. Quesnay, in his original version of the tableau, envisioned a country in which agriculture yields a net profit of 100 per cent. After assuming an agricultural investment in one farm of 600 *livres* of capital per year, he attempts to trace the flow of profit with the passage of time. The money first goes to the landlord, who spends 50 per cent in agricultural produce and 50 per cent in other expenses. In Quesnay's tableau, the 600 *livres* are traced from a central column to both right and left— 300 in each direction. The 300 *livres* of the left are reinvested in agriculture and again yield a profit of 100 per cent. This new 300 *livres* is placed in the central column where it is again divided right and left, resulting in a further investment of 150 *livres* in agriculture. This process is continued. The right side of the tableau is reserved for payments made for manufacturing costs, shelter, food, interest on capital, domestic servants, transportation, and the like. Half of this is spent on products of the soil and is transmitted to the left column. The other half is consumed "unproductively."[2]

Central to the construction of Quesnay's tableau was the notion that every economic universe or "economy" is a system

---

[2] Cf. Henry Higgs, *The Physiocrats* (New York: The Macmillan Company, 1896), pp. 38–39.

of variables that are interrelated so that a change in one involves a more or less determinate change in each of the others. In addition, the economy is conceived of as having a circular flow of income and expenditures. What producers spend on production becomes the income of consumers which, in turn, becomes income for producers and the source of new expenditures on production, and so on. And finally, the tableau assumes that there exists within the economy some unique set of relative values of all the variables, which values establish a condition of "general equilibrium." When this state of affairs has been reached, all participants in the economy will have attained their relative *optimal* economic situations (that is, income of satisfactions).[3]

Quesnay did *not*, of course, suggest that this unique set of variables should or could be specified and administered by some central planning body. On the contrary, he has been described as the most important of all the "founding fathers" of the "Maximum Doctrine of Perfect Competition"—that is, he felt that if everyone were allowed to act freely in his own individual self-interest while conditions of perfect competition prevailed, maximum satisfaction of wants for all members of society would result. As one might expect, Quesnay did not make any attempt to prove this thesis. Apparently he did not believe it required any explicit proof. "He manifestly thought that if every individual strives to realize maximum satisfaction, then all individuals will 'of course' achieve maximum satisfaction."[4]

For our purpose, it is Quesnay's methodology, rather than his economic conclusions, that is of primary interest. His tableau was the first instrument ever devised to provide an explicit description of the concept of economic equilibrium—a picture of how all, rather than simply two or more, economic phenomena were interrelated, how they hung together.[5]

His picture, of course, is as poor a likeness of his own world as it is of our world. The simplifications he achieved were purchased at the price of gross distortions of reality.

---

[3] Cf. Overton H. Taylor, *A History of Economic Thought* (New York: McGraw-Hill Book Company, 1960), p. 21.

[4] Joseph A. Schumpeter, *History of Economic Analysis* (New York: Oxford University Press, Inc., 1954), p. 233.

[5] *Ibid.*, p. 242.

Almost two centuries after Quesnay began his efforts, Wassily W. Leontief made an attempt to construct a Tableau Economique for the United States. This effort was, however, less ambitious in scope than that of Quesnay. It is entitled "The Structure of the American Economy 1919–1929," and addresses itself to an effort to apply the economic theory of general equilibrium—or, as its author prefers to call it, general interdependence—to "an empirical study of interrelations among the different parts of the national economy as revealed through covariations of prices, outputs, investments and incomes."[6]

Leontief notes that the interdependence of the economy is obvious to anyone who has observed the increase in demand for groceries in Detroit when automobile sales in New York increase, or how a shutdown of Pennsylvania coal mines paralyzes New England textile mills. He agrees with critics of the theory of general interdependence when they assert that this theory cannot possibly cope with the total complexity of real-life economic processes. But he has little patience with these same critics when instead of trying to refine the theory or strengthen its inadequate base of factual information they proceed to use intuition or less adequate theory to solve the very same problems.

The heart of the matter, of course, lies in the words "very same." If you can construct a model of the economy (or of anything else) consisting of a number of linear equations, then it may be simply ridiculous to attempt to answer questions about the *very same* economy with tools or techniques or theories that are less accurate. If accuracy is your sole criterion of effectiveness, and a complete mathematical model is available, then "intuition," "common sense," or "practical experience" all seem to represent nonsense at essentially the same level of generality. However, even if a complete model were available, it is by no means always the case that accuracy is the only problem. Urgency and limited availability of perfect computational facilities inevitably raise questions about possibilities for finding *approximate* solutions. These solutions seem to be found through the use of those unfashionable mechanisms called "intuition" or "common sense."

---

[6] Wassily W. Leontief, *The Structure of the American Economy: 1919–1929* (Cambridge, Mass.: Harvard University Press, 1941), p. 3.

But in our own world, linear programming has become one of the more respectable tools available to formalist designers.

Linear programming "is a method for calculating the best plan for achieving stated objectives in a situation in which resources are limited. As such it is a method for solving the classic problem of economizing, whether in the context of an entire economy, in that of a government program, or in a single firm."[7]

With respect to the problems of a firm, it is possible to solve some very practical problems through the use of linear programming. Suppose, for example, that a firm maintains factories and warehouses in different geographical locations. Suppose that the output of each factory is a predictable quantity and that the demands made on each warehouse are also predictable. If you now want to determine how many factory products you should ship to what warehouse during a given period of time, linear programming will help you minimize the size of your transportation bills. Or, suppose you want to decide whether an extra shift should be added at a factory, or whether a new machine should be acquired, or if prices should be changed to increase sales, or how to spend your advertising money, or where to send your sales force, or what combination of products you ought to produce—linear programming will help you, providing you have a set of reliable figures to use for your basic assumptions.

Linear programming, in short, is a mathematical model, and like any other mathematical model it is useful for tracing out the implications of a given set of assumptions. These assumptions, in the field of system or organization or societal design, relate to predicted system states and predicted situations. Linear programming itself is the analytic technique that makes the bridge between these two sets of predictions. It provides the best or optimal answer.

Fundamental to the linear programming model is the assumption that the system being designed is composed of a number of basic functions referred to as "activities." These are the representative building blocks that are recombined in varying

---

[7] Robert Dorfman, Paul A. Samuelson, and Robert M. Solow, *Linear Programming and Economic Analysis* (New York: McGraw-Hill Book Company, 1958), p. 130.

amounts to form a new system. The specific amounts of the different types of activities to be performed by the new system are called its program.[8]

The optimization or best-answer idea is a familiar one to mathematicians who use calculus and to economists who use marginal utility analysis. In linear programming, however, it is not necessary that the specifications for the system be precise. It is only necessary for them to indicate minimal requirements. "The side conditions are inequalities rather than equations. That is, they do not state that X must equal 500 but only that X must be no less than 500."[9]

Linear programming becomes quite useful in connection with the task of constructing simplified "simulation" models and exercises for use in analyzing, designing, or improving the effectiveness of systems.

To construct a complete model of a real system by means of a mathematical model, it is necessary to determine that the range of situations in which action can occur has been accurately predicted, that the various states of the system which will be confronted with these situations have been accurately predicted, and that there exist analytic or mathematical techniques which can provide solutions to the models constructed. When all of these elements are present, there are good reasons for believing that simulation can provide solutions significantly better than intuition, common sense, or practical experience.

Examining a typical "business simulation" may help clarify this point. Such an exercise may begin with four or five participants who are seated at a table in a room and asked to imagine that they constitute the board of directors of a company engaged in the manufacture and sale of some specific product. The participants are then told that they will be holding quarterly meetings (the dimension of time is compressed so that a three-month duration in the real world corresponds to perhaps ten minutes in the

---

[8] Cf. George B. Dantzig, "Concepts, Origins and Use of Linear Programming," *Proceedings of the First International Conference on Operation Research* (Baltimore: Conference Committee on Operations Research Society of America, 1957), p. 100.

[9] William J. Baumol, *Economic Theory and Operation Analysis,* 2nd ed. (Englewood Cliffs, N.J.: Prentice-Hall, Inc., 1965), p. 73.

exercise). At each quarterly meeting they will be expected to make decisions about building a plant, increasing total production capacity, hiring salesmen, investing in research and development, advertising, scheduling production, assigning salesmen to market areas, and so on. At each quarterly meeting they will also receive information about the progress of the business, which presumably has been affected by decisions they have made. So, for example, they will receive reports about the total sales volume their firm has achieved, and details about the company's financial status.

Now, it is theoretically possible for a godlike figure—one who is not a participant, but who is located outside the game situation; who knows the details of the world in which these participants are being asked to live; who can, because of this knowledge, traverse the time dimension with no difficulty; who knows everything that has transpired in this world—it is theoretically possible for such a figure to use the technique of linear programming and determine what decisions our board of directors should make to maximize their sales and profits. The unhappy fact is, of course, that the participants are *not* in this godlike position. Their knowledge of the world in which they live is at best quite limited. If they rely upon past experience in the game to generate a picture of the future world, they will be disappointed because of the relatively short time at their disposal and the limited data upon which to base "scientific" judgments. If they rely upon experience gained outside the exercise situation to provide cues, they will characteristically be severely shocked. Real-estate men who decide to invest large sums of the firm's capital in advertising because it works in the real-estate business will find that they go bankrupt because they haven't provided sufficient funds to produce the product; public-utility executives who conservatively neglect to invest funds for advertising will find that they have warehouses full of product but no sales; research and development executives who invest in research and development but neglect production and sales will also find themselves bankrupt.

From the point of view of the designers of the exercise, it is, of course, possible to arrange the exercise parameters so that, in the long run, optimal decisions by participants will require some specific allocations of investment among the various activities on which it is legal for the board of directors to spend their funds. The advantage the exercise designers have, of course, is that they can specify and hold constant the environment in which all behavior within the exercise will occur. In systems where this is possible, the linear programming model is quite valuable indeed. Where it is not possible, the use of this model as an "approximation" is simply a fancy way of talking about intuition. Indeed it may be a woefully inadequate substitute for common sense.

THE GAME THEORY MODEL

One superficially plausible method for designing a system begins with considering the problems of one man on a desert island. One designs a system to meet his requirements and then extrapolates the design parameters—if necessary, to the whole of mankind. This method has the advantage of beginning with the simple and moving to the complex. It has the ring of science and methodological rigor. It seems to have the sanction of Occam's razor. It has only one discernible defect: It won't work.

The game theory model helps us to understand why.

The method of one man on an island is the Robinson Crusoe method popularized through the efforts of the so-called Austrian school of economists. Crusoe's economic problem is to maximize his satisfaction. He has certain wants or needs or personal requirements, and has available to himself a limited number of commodities of various kinds. His task is to allocate the commodities in such a fashion as to achieve an optimal degree of well-being. But as John von Neumann and Oskar Morgenstern pointed out a couple of decades ago,[10] when Crusoe finds himself in a social exchange economy—when he finds himself embedded in a system that includes other people—life becomes very different and so do his problems. He still tries to achieve an optimum

---

[10] John von Neumann and Oskar Morgenstern, *Theory of Games and Economic Behavior* (Princeton, N.J.: Princeton University Press, 1943), pp. 11–12.

solution, but to do so he finds he must exchange goods and services with other people. And once other people enter the scene, what happens to friend Crusoe depends upon what other people do as well as upon what he himself does. The game now includes many Crusoes who find they are no longer lords of a predictable and specifiable universe. Life becomes a mishmash of maximization problems—and is no longer simple. Where the original Crusoe was presented with an array of more or less fixed data (describing the facts of his physical environment), the many Crusoes are presented with an additional set of data. These data consist of the product of other Crusoes' actions and desires. An example of this is the phenomenon of prices. The action of each Crusoe now becomes influenced by his expectations about these actions and desires, while these reflect modifications resulting from what the others expect from him.

In the face of this increasing complexity, it becomes the task of game theory to discover the "mathematically complete principles which define 'rational behavior' for the participants in a social economy, and to derive from them the general characteristics of that behavior."[11]

In brief, game theory is essentially a theory about the outcome of ordinary games of strategy such as chess or cards—assuming that the games are played by thoroughly "rational" persons.[12] It is interesting to note, however, that as of the time this is being written, the contribution made by game theory to actual strategy in over-the-board chess play, or to the general theory of chess, is essentially zero. The reason for this is quite simple. Game theory addresses itself directly to situations of the kind we have called "established." And these, of course, represent a very restricted range of possible situations. They are characterized by predicted ranges of events, predicted system states, and the availability of an analytic technology that can provide determined (that is, probabilities of 1.0) or stochastic (probabilities of something less than 1.0) solutions to analytic problems.

---

[11] *Ibid.*, p. 31.
[12] Cf. Kenneth J. Arrow, "Mathematical Models in the Social Sciences," *The Policy Sciences,* ed. Daniel Lerner and Harold D. Lasswell (Stanford, Calif.: Stanford University Press, 1951), p. 139.

Thus, for example, if there were available a computer with sufficient capacity to trace the implications of every tree resulting from every possible move that could legally be made by each chess player, then we might talk about the existence of an appropriate analytic technology. This technology could provide to each potential player a handbook of things to do under every possible situation arising in over-the-board play.

In the absence of such technology, and it is nowhere on the horizon at this writing, it is impossible to make any definitive statements about what, in fact, is the best move for any given player at his turn. This, of course, scarcely keeps people from playing chess—or, as we have previously observed, from winning consistently—but the popular notion that game theory at this stage of its development is of any help is pure mythology.

In game-theoretic terms, chess is a "two-person, zero-sum" game; i.e., what one of two players wins, the other player loses. The algebraic sum of their efforts is zero. Ticktacktoe is another example of a two-person, zero-sum game. In addition, both ticktacktoe and chess are classified as games of "complete information," that is, all of the formal history of the game—the moves each side has made—is available to each player. Thus, in game-theoretic terms, both these games are regarded as being of the same "species"—each player in theory could select a "strategy" at the beginning of the game, which would consist of a complete "program" in which all possible answers of the opponent to each of one's moves are considered and one's own reply to each of these is stated.[13]

Within this theoretical framework, the fact that such a program is not available for the game of chess because of the lack of a technology for preparing the necessary program constitutes a trivial difficulty. Such a program is available for the game of ticktacktoe, and indeed could be written by any neophyte computer programmer a few hours after beginning his introductory course in computer programming. Thus, within the framework of *game theory*, chess presents no theoretical problem. Within

---

[13] Cf. Anatol Rapoport, "Uses and Limitations of Mathematical Models in Social Science," *Symposium on Sociological Theory,* ed. Llewellyn Gross (New York: Harper & Row, Publishers, Inc., 1959), pp. 366–367.

the framework of *system design theory,* however, the problem of chess presents enormous theoretical problems. It is a characteristic of many systems that the necessary technology for preparing a complete strategy is never available within the time period during which the system must be designed, or indeed during the period of its entire existence.

No mathematical statement exists from which one could obtain a set of values showing the "score" after each move. If white moves his pawn instead of his knight, what numerical difference does it make? What theoretical payoff exists if he adopts one alternative versus the other—assuming that neither move results in an immediate or discernible termination of the game? The answer, of course, is that no one knows, and game theory does not provide an answer.

RIGOROUSLY RATIONAL MODELS

The linear programming model and the game theory model are usually viewed as part of the model species called "mathematical." But this, in turn, is a highly ambiguous concept. At least three different meanings of the term "mathematical model" are clearly distinguishable.[14] In the first place, it may refer to any quantitative statement about regularities in the empirical world. If we observe that the population of a country has been increasing at a given rate, the expression containing all the necessary information to predict future population figures may be described as a mathematical model. This model is, in essence, a theory about the world and is very useful as long as it remains an accurate description of this world. If, for example, people start to use birth-control measures for the first time, the birth-rate predictions in the theory may become wrong and the total population predictions wrong.

The term "mathematical model" is also used to refer to a set of fundamentally tautological truths about numbers. This, of course, can be very useful for purposes of analyzing the implica-

---

[14] Cf. May Brodbeck, "Models, Meaning, and Theories," *ibid.,* pp. 391–392.

tions of any given statement made about established situations. The model in this context literally helps us to know what it is that we know.

Finally, mathematical models are used to construct "formalizations" of theories. This consists of a process in which the descriptive terms of a theory are replaced by letters. This yields a formal statement that has not been given descriptive content. An example of the formalization of a linear relationship is $y = ax + b$. With these three meanings of mathematical model in mind, if we now try to specify the precise sense in which the linear programming and game theory models are mathematical models, we encounter some interesting difficulties.

Thus, Quesnay's linear programming tableau, for example, begins by purporting to be, in effect, an empirical description of economic reality. It proceeds, however, to become an arithmetic representation of an economic theory. Leontief's tableau of the American economy performs essentially the same tasks, albeit with the aid of an enormously more sophisticated statistical and conceptual apparatus. In a purely formal sense, however, linear programming provides us simply with a way of minimizing or maximizing a quantity in the face of certain specifiable restraints; that is, it is a set of analytic or tautological truths about numbers.

Now there can be little quarrel with each of these efforts as long as they remain within the bounds of their individual frameworks. However, if we implicitly claim empirical credence for a statement primarily on the basis that it is sound in its formalized expression, we are in trouble. If, for example, we use linear programming or game theory to *design* a system that we hope will exist some day, we must rely upon the soundness of the *empirical* theory that is used as its basis, rather than simply upon the adequacy of our symbolic manipulations.

Social theorists are quite familiar with this kind of difficulty. It was Max Weber, in his discussion of the "ideal type," who pointed up the problem most clearly. The ideal type is a tool containing concepts as well as summaries of empirical data. Weber noted the potential danger of confusing these two by using the discipline of economics as an illustration. Economics was, on the one hand, a technique in that it viewed reality in terms of a specific, consistent point of view—the "wealth" of a population. On the other hand, however, it is much more than a technique in that historically it became integrated into the *Weltanschauung* of the eighteenth century, which consisted of a faith in the "rationalizability" of reality. This had the important consequence of obstructing the discovery that the things that had been regarded as self-evident were, in fact, the very things that were problematic.[15]

Thus, classical economic theory did not represent an abstract theory. In point of fact, it presented an idealized picture of events in the commodity market under conditions of exchange, free competition, and narrowly defined rational conduct. "Relations and events of historical life were selected and formed onto an internally consistent system. Classical economics presented an idealization of certain elements of historical reality. Its 'theory' was actually a utopia-like construct."[16]

This, of course, is another way of saying that classical economic theory was empirically false, however "true" its internal logic may have been. If, indeed, this was the case—if classical economic theory was, in fact, false as a description of historical reality—then the trap lay in the very rigor of its internal logic. If you wish to choose instruments of analysis at a given level of exactness, then you mustn't extrapolate your findings to regions where the data are sloppy—unless you have good information about the parameters of this sloppiness. As Harold Garfinkel has pointed out, the ability to act "rationally"—to project alternative plans of action, to determine priorities, and so forth—"depends upon the fact that the person must be able literally to take for granted, to take under trust, a vast array of the features of the social order. In order to treat rationally the 1/10 of his situation that, like an iceberg, appears above the water, he must be able to treat the 9/10 that lies below the water as an unquestioned and, even more interestingly, as an unquestionable background of

---

[15] Cf. Max Weber, *The Methodology of the Social Sciences,* ed. and trans. Edward A. Shils and Henry A. Finch (New York: Free Press of Glencoe, Inc., 1949), p. 85.

[16] Don Martindale, "Sociological Theory and the Ideal Type," *Symposium on Sociological Theory, op. cit.,* p. 67.

matters that are demonstrably relevant to his calculation, but which appear without being noticed."[17]

Garfinkel reminds us that sociologists have words for these taken-for-granted features of situations. Examples of these words are mores and folkways. It is only against the background of these features that it is possible to decide that a specific course of action, occurring in a specific society, is reasonable or rational.

It is precisely here that formalist utopian designers tend to go astray. They pour all of their ingenuity and energy into the top of Garfinkel's iceberg, while blithely assuming that the subsurface structure will adopt precisely the form necessary to support the top.

The incorporation of incongruous folkways, mores, and basic values is probably one of the most pervasive anomalies to be found in utopian romances, in historical efforts to establish utopian communities, or in otherwise sophisticated attempts to design contemporary systems through the use of mathematical techniques. In many cases this has been used as the basis for satire or broad comedy—especially in utopian romances. But the humor tends to become truly "unconscious," since the specific nature of the incongruities is characteristically omitted from consideration.

The failure of Robert Owen's New Harmony community is a case in point. The inconsistencies existing among Sir Thomas More's Utopians is another one. And the unconscious satire existing in Francis Bacon's *New Atlantis* is a third. Let us briefly examine each of these.

Robert Owen was no mere visionary reformer; he was a practical and successful businessman. As a cotton mill manager in New Lanark, Scotland, early in the nineteenth century, he earned his spurs as an entrepreneur. In the process of earning a considerable return on his invested capital, he simultaneously raised the standard of living for hundreds of families and destitute children. His utopian plans were formalized in a report he prepared for a Committee on Poor Laws appointed by the House of Commons and in several additional documents. His basic point

---

[17] Harold Garfinkel, "The Rational Properties of Scientific and Common Sense Activities," *Behavioral Science*, V, No. 1 (January 1960), 82.

was quite simple. It consisted of the assertion that the introduction of machinery was displacing manual labor. Since the wage bill of the country was reduced, workers were unable to buy enough of the things they needed and these things remained unsold in barns and warehouses throughout the country.

His remedy, too, was quite simple. He suggested that communities of about a thousand persons each should be established on an area covering about 1000 to 1500 acres of land. The inhabitants would live in large buildings built in the form of a square. Owen described the location of the buildings, the use of common dining rooms, dormitories, libraries, schools, and the like. Indeed, the entire scheme is strongly reminiscent of Fourier's phalanstery plan (although apparently these two schemes were devised completely independently from each other). In Owen's community the inhabitants would engage in both agriculture and manufacturing, using the latest and best models of available machinery and equipment.

Owen did more than make a plan; he seriously tried to implement his ideas. In 1824, he bought some land in Indiana and established the community of New Harmony.

Many reasons have been given to account for the failure of the New Harmony community. Perhaps the most simple summary would say: He forgot about the bottom of the iceberg—his formalist model was woefully incomplete because it omitted from consideration the myriads of variables introduced by the behavior of participants in his system, the unpredicted situations with which the system would be faced, and the lack of a sufficiently sophisticated and analytic technology to provide reliable solutions to the problems the system would encounter.

Persons who had long been accustomed to obtaining as much as possible from society for the least possible expenditure of effort were now asked to work harder and (at least temporarily) to receive less. Persons whose history of interpersonal relations had taught them to distrust everyone in every economic transaction were now asked to trust their administrators and fellow residents without reservation. Idealistic intellectuals who had learned to despise manual labor were now asked to view it as the highest form of patriotic duty. The icebergs multiplied endlessly. They might be labeled covetousness, greed, and pride.

Among Sir Thomas More's Utopians, there presumably was no room for covetousness, greed, or pride. The father of every family or every householder was authorized to take anything he needed without payment of money, credit, or anything else in exchange. Since an abundance of all material goods existed, why should anything be denied him? Or why, for that matter, should anyone take more than he needed in the first place?

Pride, among the Utopians, was seen as stemming from scarcity. If you eliminate scarcity then the notion that conspicuous consumption was a soul-satisfying activity would simply disappear. The design of Utopia eliminates the problem of conspicuous consumption through the mechanism of plenty for all. This should settle the matter, but it doesn't. Indeed, the Utopians take elaborate precautions to insure that the hoi polloi do not covet the wrong things. Although they eat and drink from earthen and glass vessels, they make their chamber pots and probably spittoons out of gold and silver. They also use gold chains to tie their bondsmen, hang rings of gold to the ears and around the necks of offenders, and also make these offenders wear gold rings. They don't make a point of collecting diamonds or pearls; but if they do find such things, they use them to dress up infants. Adults, therefore, would be ashamed of wearing these ornaments—they represent kid stuff.

Why all this should continue to be necessary in a society that has eliminated pride, conspicuous consumption, and all the rest is not made clear. The structure of values held by More's Utopians is clearly *not* congruous with the system he so carefully designed.

Francis Bacon's *New Atlantis* illustrates our anomaly in terms that are quite different. Bacon's concern, in this fictional utopia, was to describe what in twentieth-century America might be called an ideal "think factory." This institute, called Salomon's House, had the advantage of sending several representatives abroad every twelve years to obtain knowledge "especially of the sciences, arts, manufactures, and inventions of all the world, and withal to bring unto us books, instruments, and patterns of every kind . . . thus you see we maintain a trade, not for gold, silver or jewels, nor for silks, nor for spices, nor any other commodity of matter; but only for God's first creature, which was light. . . ."[18] Given this general orientation, one might well envision an institute completely devoted to the aims of science and inhabited by devotees who are indifferent to material ostentation and who, perhaps, would refuse to take even the necessary time from their researches to prepare gilded chamber pots.

What do we find?

One of the "fathers" of Salomon's House makes his entry. "He was carried in a rich chariot, without wheels, litter-wise. The chariot was all cedar, gilt and adorned with crystal; save that the fore-end had panels of sapphires, set in borders of gold, and the hinder-end the like of emeralds of Peru color. There was also a sum of gold, radiant upon the top, in the midst; and on the top before a small cherub of gold with wings displayed. He had before him fifty attendants, young men all, in white satin loose coats up to the mid-leg, and stockings of white silk, and shoes of blue velvet. . . ."[19] And so on.

The necessity for all this pomp, given the goals of Salomon's House, is never made clear.

Pomp and chamber pots are trivia, but the kind of thinking that produces lapses of the sort we have illustrated can result in the most deadly serious of consequences. The history of utopian design efforts seems to reveal a high correlation between the use of rigorous rationality within a system design and the omission of significant elements from the system model.

From time to time utopian designers are chastised for expecting abstract or idealized social systems to work miracles while forgetting that social systems are composed of human beings and that the systems cannot be better than those who participate in them. The suggested solution to this dilemma may take the form of an assertion that only through a better understanding of the basic principles of human psychology or social behavior can realistic reform efforts be made.[20]

---

[18] Francis Bacon, *New Atlantis,* Harvard Classics, Vol. III, Charles W. Eliot, ed. (New York: The Crowell-Collier Publishing Co., 1909), p. 171.

[19] *Ibid., p.* 180.

[20] Cf. Franz Alexander, *Our Age of Unreason,* rev. ed. (Philadelphia: J. B. Lippincott Co., 1951), p. 28.

To a hard-boiled contemporary designer of large-scale systems, this assertion can be stood on its head and made to appear as an invitation for more indiscriminate automation—to get rid of unreliable human components. But the real force of the assertion arises from the insight that, even in the most narrowly circumscribed of large-scale systems, the problem of dealing with emergent situations recurs. The devices we use for dealing with these situations *may* consist of better educated or more sensitive people. But other alternatives exist, and we shall discuss some of them in the following pages. They do *not* include simple mimicry of bad utopian habits. The road to optimum system design is not paved with artificial and untrue assumptions about the characteristics of the world we live in. These, however, are the pitfalls that too often accompany the use of rigorous rationality.

RITUAL MODELING

Psychologist Donald N. Michael has given us the phrase "ritualized rationality" to describe certain techniques used for solving problems in the field of arms control and disarmament. Ritualized rationality consists of "undertaking elaborate rational, logical or mathematical exercises which often are not used or are not useful."[21] Indeed, Michael tells us, these exercises frequently are not used simply because they were not intended to be used in the first place. They are more properly seen as magic-like rituals invoked by confused and frustrated decision makers or advisers to decision makers. With respect to arms control and disarmament, the luxury of ritual is possible when solutions to problems of war and peace are neither urgently required nor urgently desired by the decision makers involved. Thus ritual modeling may be preferred to more realistic problem solving when war is seen as being unlikely—especially when the readjustments required by arms reduction solutions might involve giving up desirable status quo's.

---

[21] Donald N. Michael, "Ritualized Rationality and Arms Control," *Bulletin of the Atomic Scientists,* XVII, No. 2 (February 1961), 72.

Now, in many ways Michael is unfair in singling out logic and mathematics when discussing ritual modeling. Indeed, one might well use his phrase to describe psychological analyses that are ritualistically Freudian, Jungian, Adlerian, and so on, and are used to avoid the necessity for logical or empirical or mathematical analysis. The interesting point for our purposes is not the fact that logic or mathematics is used. Rather, it is that any method or technique—scientific, mathematical, psychological, or religious—may be invoked as a substitute for problem solving. It happens that in many contemporary decision-making circles, slide-rule bearing "whiz kids" have become fashionable. In other times and in other places it has been German epistemologists, Viennese psychiatrists, American combat pilots, or New England payroll-meeting businessmen who were the pets of fashion.

And by no means must all analyses resulting in incorrect or nonuseful statements about the real world be condemned as ritualistic. Some analyses, formalist or otherwise, are not based upon ritual modeling; they are simply wrong or not useful. But a central question that we must answer in order to understand any ritual modeling effort is: For whom is this analysis *not* useful and why?

Perhaps the most extensive use of ritual modeling throughout recorded history is to be found in the work of the classical utopian designers. Many of these designs were not intended to be useful, in the sense that the designer did not expect the reader to use his fantasy as a blueprint for building a new society. They were, however, useful as social criticism. They did this by extrapolating the characteristics of an existing social system to ludicrous lengths. This made them useful only in the sense of providing social satire. But social satire may be a useful function indeed—for some portions of the population.

Ritual modeling is also useful, of course, as an alternative to action. A parliamentary device that has proved far more effective than the filibuster is the device of delaying action until a ritual modeling job has been completed. Frequently these efforts are called "studies," or "investigation," or even "research."

Continued public controversies about the relative merits of manned bombers versus missiles highlight the kind of difficulty that stems from an uncritical reliance upon ritual modeling. The protagonists in this particular conflict consist of some "whiz kids" on the one hand, and professional military officers (possibly former combat pilots) on the other. How accurate is a missile? How effective is a bomber? Both protagonists have available (for public consumption) volumes of analyses purporting to prove, in very precise terms, conclusions exactly opposite to each other. One should not simply assume that the analyses are stupid or malicious. In most cases they are simple non sequiturs. Their function is to impress rather than to inform. But they can be used only to impress those who demand to be impressed. They are the results rather than the cause of ignorance.

In a very real sense, each of the protagonists is using a model as the basis for his conclusions. The model in each case is restricted to a consideration of some limited range of phenomena. Depending upon what aspect of the world the protagonists choose to ignore, it is possible for them to arrive at completely different conclusions. They characteristically address themselves to different sets of established situations. The fact that these situations may never be found in the world of "reality" is seen simply as a problem for those who wish to be realists. And, of course, it is neither necessary nor desirable that everyone in the world be a realist. Indeed, it is quite possible to make a strong case for the continued existence of such potential nonrealists as academicians, coupon-clipping investors, and vagabonds—to say nothing of philosophers, psychiatrists, combat pilots, businessmen, or scientists. A problem arises only when a nonobvious reversal of roles occurs. When the pure scientist tries to pass as a realist, or for that matter, when the pure realist tries to pass as a scientist —it is useful to invoke the practice of ritual modeling to validate one's role. The most fashionable techniques available these days are formalist approaches. They typically lend themselves to easy quantification and can readily borrow the mana of the computer to impress the uninitiated.

RECONDITE MODELS

By this time it should be apparent that although the word model normally evokes images of clarity and simplicity, the formalist approach to system design frequently results in the use of models whose meaning remains obscure and even mysterious. Consider, if you will, the models of Kahn.

Since we began this chapter by describing Herman Kahn as one of the most vocal of recent spokesmen for the formalist approach to system design, it seems appropriate to review the models he uses in his discussions of the pros and cons of thermonuclear war.

In a document issued in 1957, while he was still at the RAND Corporation, Kahn, together with Irwin Mann, undertook to present "ten common pitfalls" of system analysis.[22] The first pitfall described in this document is called "modelism"—being more interested in the model than one is in the real world. This results in the study of irrelevant or over-idealized questions rather than answers to important policy questions. Analysts get trapped in this pitfall because trying to provide answers to important policy questions may get one involved in some "mathematically untidy questions."

Another of the pitfalls listed in the Kahn and Mann document is one called "overambition." This seems to be something roughly the inverse of the modelism pitfall. "It is essential," we are told, "for the analyst to stick to problems on which he really can give sound and extremely defensible advice."[23]

It is on this last point that Kahn becomes most vulnerable in his *On Thermonuclear War*. One of the pieces of advice provided in this book is the one saying that enlarged civil defense and counterforce capabilities are advantageous to "us." The problem glossed over, however, is the crucial one of specifying the criteria of advantage. In a penetrating analysis, J. David

---

[22] Herman Kahn and Irwin Mann, *Ten Common Pitfalls* (RM 1937) (Santa Monica, Calif.: The RAND Corporation, 1957).

[23] *Ibid.*, p. 33.

Singer[24] has developed the thesis that enlarged civil defense and counterforce capabilities may be quite disadvantageous to "us." Thus, if the criterion used is one that seeks to minimize the probability of nuclear war, then it is important to include in one's calculations the high probability that the counterforce and civil defense capability may be provocative. If the criterion used is a "don't-let-the-enemy-bluff-us" one, then the counterforce capability may be useful. But Singer points to the utter absurdity of employing a don't-let-the-enemy-bluff-us criterion, if it clashes with a prevent-the-war criterion. Of course, Singer is making implicit assumptions about what is or is not absurd—as is Kahn. Neither one of them undertakes to explore the nature of these assumptions. They remain as almost totally submerged icebergs, yet they constitute the most significant part of any analysis to be made on the subject.

In short, Kahn is using a highly recondite model. His vulnerability does not lie simply in the issue of whether he is "correct" or not. The point is that however much he qualifies his statements, the message communicated to his readers contains a strong implication that the model of international relations he uses contains all relevant parameters and that his conclusions are based upon a careful and even a "mathematical" analysis of these parameters. This, of course, is simply not true, as Kahn himself recognizes in the following passage:

> Every senior man in Washington or other allied capital must have at least five people a day come into his office with *the* solution to his problem, and since almost all of these solutions have incompatible premises, it is quite likely that four of the five people are wrong and very possibly all five are. The problem is to devise solutions which will withstand analysis (and hopefully actual experience). I do not have the space in this book to discuss how in fact to design "good" systems and how to test these designs.[25]

The formalist approach to system design is the approach of

---

[24] J. David Singer, "The Strategic Dilemma: Probability Versus Utility. A Review of Herman Kahn, *On Thermonuclear War*," *The Journal of Conflict Resolution*, V, No. 2 (June 1961), 203.

[25] Herman Kahn, *On Thermonuclear War* (Princeton, N.J.: Princeton University Press, 1960), pp. 549–550.

preference when the situations to be confronted are clearly established in nature. To use it or imply that it is being used in other than these situations is to invite misunderstandings of the kind that have always bedeviled the designers of formalist systems, organizations, and societies.

4

HEURISTIC DESIGNS

HEURISTIC PROGRAMMING

Perhaps the most significant advance made in computer programming technology during recent years consists of the development called "heuristic programming."

The difference between heuristic programming and more traditional forms of computer programming is a difference in the "guarantees" provided under each of the two methods. The traditional form of a computer program is an algorithm—a set of systematic procedures guaranteeing solution of the problem to a specific degree of accuracy. Heuristic programs incorporate "rules of thumb" or principles into computer programs, and these rules of thumb carry no such guarantees.[1]

The development of heuristic programming is correctly attributable to the efforts of three men: Allen Newell, Herbert A. Simon, and J. C. Shaw. Simon, however, graciously assigns pri-

---

[1] Herbert A. Simon, "Modeling Human Mental Processes," *Proceedings of the Western Joint Computer Conference, May 9–11, 1961,* p. 114.

ority to the work of others who were primarily concerned with the problem of "pattern recognition." Simon observes that the methods used to distinguish patterns involved essentially the use of rules of thumb selected by a computer over a series of trials on the sole basis that they seemed to work, that is, they made discriminations of the sort desired by the computer programmer.[2]

Be that as it may, the most sophisticated example of available heuristic programs is the Newell, Shaw, and Simon effort called General Problem Solver (GPS).[3] There are, of course, and have been many other heuristic programs that have attempted to do such things as: compose music through the use of some principles of classical counterpoint;[4] design electric motors and transformers through the use of design principles used by experienced engineers;[5] play chess through using principles of good play used by experienced chess players.[6]

GPS differs from these previous efforts in that it represents the "first computer program aimed at describing the problem solving techniques used by humans that are independent of the subject matter of the problem."[7]

In this sense, GPS may be viewed as an effort to replicate the behavior of human beings when they are faced with a situation for which formalist methods are clearly inappropriate. It postulates several alternate problem solving principles and proceeds to incorporate them in computer programs for dealing with problems in such specific areas as symbolic logic and chess.

One of these principles is called means-end or functional analysis. This is illustrated by the following kind of common sense logic:

---

[2] *Ibid.*, p. 114.

[3] A. Newell, J. C. Shaw, and H. A. Simon, "A General Problem-Solving Program for a Computer," *Computers and Automation,* VIII, No. 7 (July 1959), 10–17.

[4] L. A. Hiller and L. M. Isaacson, *Experimental Music* (New York: McGraw-Hill Book Company, 1959).

[5] G. L. Goodwin, "Digital Computers Tap out Designs for Large Motors Fast," *Power* (April 1958).

[6] A. Newell, J. C. Shaw, and H. A. Simon, "Chess Playing Programs and the Problem of Complexity," *IBM Journal of Research and Development,* II, No. 4 (October 1958), 320–335.

[7] Herbert A. Simon, "Modeling Human Mental Processes," *op. cit.,* p. 115.

I want to take my son to nursery school. What's the difference between what I have and what I want? One of distance. What changes distance? My automobile. My automobile won't work. What's needed to make it work? A new battery. What has new batteries? An auto repair shop. I want the repair shop to put in a new battery, but the shop doesn't know I need one. What is the difficulty? One of communication. What allows communication? A telephone. . . .[8]

To perform its functional analysis, the computer program defines several entities. These are called, "expressions," "differences between expressions," "operators," "goals," "subgoals," and "methods." The prototype problem it undertakes to solve in this mode is expressed as follows: "given expression a and a set of admissible operators, to derive expression b."[9]

Each goal is associated with a set of methods that are procedures designed to help achieve that goal. Where subgoals are needed they are formulated, and procedures are applied to help them become realized.

Specifically, three types of goals are used for functional analysis:

1) find a way to transform expression a into expression b;
2) reduce the difference (labeled d) between expressions a and b;
3) apply an operator (called q) to expression a.[10]

Since each of the goals is associated with a method, there are three methods. To accomplish the first goal the method consists of comparing a and b to find a difference d. After finding this difference, the subgoal of reducing d is established. The result of this, hopefully, is a new expression, which is called c. Another subgoal is now invoked—the one that attempts to transform c into b. If this is successful, our mission has been accomplished.

Similarly, to accomplish the second goal, the program begins

---

[8] A. Newell, J. C. Shaw, and H. A. Simon, "A General Problem-Solving Program for a Computer," *op. cit.*, p. 12.

[9] A. Newell, J. C. Shaw, and H. A. Simon, "The Processes of Creative Thinking" (*P-1320*) (Santa Monica, Calif.: The RAND Corporation, rev. 28 January 1959), p. 37.

[10] *Ibid.*, pp. 37–38.

by looking for an operator that can reduce d and ends by setting up the goal of applying the operator.

To achieve the third goal, the program begins by determining if the conditions are appropriate for applying the operator (called q). If the conditions are right, the operator is applied; if the conditions are not right, it proceeds to reduce the difference between a and the conditions for applying q.

The meanings of the various entities used in the program are probably clear by now, for example, an "operator" is something that can be applied to certain objects to produce different objects (as a saw applied to logs produces boards). Objects or "expressions" can be described by the features they possess and by the differences that can be observed between pairs of objects. Thus, the problem in chess, for example, is to move from one object (for example, a position on the chessboard) to an object having a particular feature (a position in which the opponent's king is checkmated).[11]

In addition to the principle of functional analysis, Newell, Shaw, and Simon use several others which they call "planning," "selection heuristics," and "processes for working backwards from the problem solution," and so on. However, they note that all of these invoke the following general principle:

> *The principle of subgoal reduction:* Make progress by substituting for the achievement of a goal the achievement of a set of easier goals.[12]

The rationale for using this principle is its similarity to what is seen as the general approach to problem solving used by human beings. In Simon's words:

> Problem solving proceeds by erecting goals, detecting differences between present situation and goal, finding in memory or by search tools or processes that are relevant to reducing differences of these particular kinds, and applying these tools or processes. Each problem generates subproblems until we find a subproblem we can solve—for which we already have a program stored in memory.

---

[11] A. Newell, J. C. Shaw, and H. A. Simon, "A General Problem-Solving Program for a Computer," *op. cit.*, p. 10.

[12] *Ibid.*, p. 11.

We proceed until, by successive solution of such subproblems, we eventually achieve our over-all goal—or give up.[13]

Since goals form the basis of heuristic programming, let us examine them in some detail. In writing a heuristic program to play chess, the goal given might be "win the game." Under some conditions of tournament play it might be given as "win if you can, but get at least a draw—don't lose," or "win—a draw is just as bad as losing." If one were to extend these efforts to the regions of "middle management" in an industrial organization, the goal might be "run this department in a manner that will insure a profit for the department at the end of the year" or "run this department in a manner that will help maximize the total corporate profit at the end of the year." However, the goal might also be stated in terms similar to the following: "Your goal is to help maximize the economic welfare of everyone on the staff of this firm. Money will help do this. Therefore, maximize profits." Faced with this kind of goal, our program might well query: "You say corporate profit will help maximize the economic welfare of everyone on the staff. Are there other things that will do this?" Or it might even assert, "You told me to maximize the economic welfare of everyone in this firm. I see several ways of doing it. Maximizing *profits* is only one way. Don't you want me to consider the other alternatives? I've got loads of ideas."

We are now faced with the necessity for either telling the computer to mind its own business (which it really has no way of doing), or reformulating our goals more precisely and saying, "Forget all that stuff about economic welfare. Just maximize profits."

The difficulty with this, of course, is simply that the computer may end by making some highly unfavorable decisions under some sets of environmental conditions. It may, for example, make operational decisions which, while maximizing corporation profits, also tend to maximize the incidence of ulcers among organizational personnel. The combined individual costs of hospital care may far exceed the net corporation profit return, but the computer will have done its job as stated.

[13] H. A. Simon, *The New Science of Management Decision* (New York: Harper & Row, Publishers, Inc., 1960), p. 27.

In short, goals, like subgoals, can usually be regarded as *means* toward achieving other goals existing at a higher level of generality. To pursue this cycle characteristically embroils us in value considerations not normally seen as coming within the purview of "science." Heuristic programming seems to avoid this dilemma. The work done to date has been addressed to the solution of problems for which the goal statements are apparently unambiguous.

One either wins a game of chess or one does not. One either proves a theorem in symbolic logic or one does not.

It will be observed, however, that things like chess and symbolic logic possess some interesting invariant features. In the first place, of course, the prime goal is fixed and unalterable during the operation of the program. In addition to this, the rules of play or of logical transformation are invariant during the operation of the program. What this means, in effect, is that although successive system environments and system states are unpredicted, the possible paths through which change can occur are known and specified. This knowledge provides one instrument for reducing uncertainty. One can now try to eliminate differences one step at a time since there hopefully exists a manageable number of steps for the process of difference-reduction.

But to engage in this sort of procedure implies some initial agreement on the terms for evaluating each new situation as it arises. In symbolic logic, this consists of asking whether the difference between two expressions has been reduced. One can determine this according to a scheme specifying exactly what is involved in a difference—is it the number of expressions, the nature of the logical operations involved, the positions of the symbols, or what? In chess it involves the making of some assumptions about the situations leading one nearer to the objective of checkmating the opponent's king. One may therefore employ a principle such as piece count—where piece count consists of assigning a numerical score to each piece (9 for the queen, 5 for the rook, and so on) and totaling these scores after each move or prospective move to evaluate the new situation presented by the move. Or, one might invoke the principle of development, defined operationally by counting the number of legal moves available to each piece on a side and totaling the number for each side. The relation between these principles and their potential conflict with each other is recognized by the chess term "gambit," which literally means "sacrificing" a pawn (or other piece) in order to achieve some other benefit (such as increased development).

The question remains, "Is the gambit *good?*" Chess players may and indeed do have strong opinions on the "goodness" of the Queen's Gambit in chess. Some say yes, some say no. A heuristic program can resolve the question by reverting to principle and deciding that piece count is more important than development, or that a given number of development points is equivalent to a given number of piece count points, or that development is more important early in the game and piece count more important in the later stages, and so on. Any particular decision made along these lines fixes the major operational goals for some definable period of time. If this period of time lasts too long, the principles may prove to be not simply less than optimal; they may in fact become completely dysfunctional.

Consider, for a moment, the probable course of events if we decide to match two chess-playing computers against each other. Assume that the same single strategic principle is given each—the principle of piece count. Assuming that no mechanism for learning exists, we may predict a random outcome to the contests between these two players. Now let us give to computer A the principle of development, in addition to the piece count principle. We may expect that computer B will be offered a variety of gambits which it will invariably accept, since to computer B every favorable exchange seems to be money in the bank. The single-minded piece count principle of computer B will unquestionably prove to be the strongest reason for his downfall.

The difference between this use of heuristics to deal with emergent situations and the use of formalist techniques should now be apparent. A computer equipped to use only formalist approaches might be programmed in a variety of ways. The most obvious way would be to try to anticipate every situation that could possibly occur in a game of chess. But, if the state of technology happens to be what it is at this writing, no available computer or set of computers would have a memory large enough to explore and usefully retain all of these situations. We must then fall back upon completely inadequate alternatives. We might, on the basis of elaborate statistical studies of past chess games, program an optimum number or sequence of moves for each of the pieces—and this might conceivably result in better-than-chance outcomes over a series of trials. Or one might simply wait and depend upon the occurrence and recognition of established situations. Since the ability of the computer to deal effectively with these is perfect, waiting for these situations to occur in an otherwise random world might prove distinctly better than chance. But in any event the computer would not engage in any learning process; it would do exactly what it was told to do.

The key to all this, of course, lies in the word "learning." The developers of heuristic programming techniques have been highly sensitive to the requirements for a learning capacity as an integral part of these techniques. The danger lies in the possibility that the learning techniques developed will tend to be directed toward the achievement of goals that have become dysfunctional in terms of some broader human purpose. What are these human purposes? How does one know when a social-system design is consistent with the achievement of human purposes? How can heuristic concepts be applied to the problems of human existence within a complex social system?

THE HEURISTIC OF LIBERTY

We have mentioned the principles Proudhon saw as the only constants in his social system. They include such things as liberty, equality, fraternity and justice. What, precisely, are these things? In what sense are they "heuristics?" What, for example, is this thing called "liberty?"

Is it an immediate datum, something that cannot be analyzed into components or reduced to simpler elements? Is it, in

short, synonymous with the state of being free, where being
free is as primary and fundamental a condition as being warm or
being pleased or being angry?[14]

If we accept this notion, then, it has been argued,[15] volumes
of familiar discourses on liberty written since the days of the
ancient Greeks are based upon a completely false set of premises.
One such false premise assumes that liberty is simply the absence
of restraint. Thomas Hobbes, utilitarians such as Jeremy Ben-
tham and John Stuart Mill, nature worshippers such as Thoreau,
philosophical anarchists, and economic conservatives all seem to
proceed from this misconception. They see liberty as being
inversely related to the amount of law in existence—and every
new law as consuming another piece of the liberty pie. Another
of these false premises confuses universal liberty with the liberty
of an individual or of a specific group. This premise provides a
rationale for restraining the opinions of radicals if one happens
to be a conservative, or for restraining the opinions of conservatives if one happens to be a radical. Still another of the false
premises involves an implicit redefinition of the term liberty and
the assumption that the new term continues to include values of
the old.

Regarding liberty as a primary datum has the strong virtue
of focusing attention upon it as an end in itself, rather than as
a means to some other end or as a subgoal. It provides us with
a simple but powerful conceptual instrument for cutting through
the mass of semantic camouflage that frequently surrounds the
term. Recent controversies in the field of civil rights have high-
lighted one of the more vicious varieties of this camouflage.
Liberty is invoked as a battle cry to protect the inalienable right
to discriminate against minority groups. In the area of economic
controversy, liberty is invoked as a battle cry to protect the
inalienable right to ignore the distress of one's fellow man. All
this is done in the name of liberty as a primary datum and it all
helps us to understand why regarding liberty as a primary

---

[14] Robert M. MacIver, "The Meaning of Liberty and Its Perversions,"
Freedom: Its Meaning, ed. Ruth Nanda Anshen (New York: Harcourt,
Brace & World, Inc., 1940), p. 279.
[15] Cf. *Ibid.,* pp. 280–285.

datum is not enough. It is continually necessary to ask, "How and for whom does the liberty bell toll?"

If we encounter difficulties in trying to use the liberty concept as a goal, subgoal, or primary datum, are we helped any by thinking of it as a right? What are we really saying when we assert that all men have a *right* to liberty? Can we discuss this dispassionately without using emotional arguments or emotionally charged words? (We should remember that although computers can replicate behavior of human beings who act in an emotional fashion, no one has yet devised a satisfactory way of demonstrating that computers can feel good, bad, happy, or unhappy about things—and it is rather difficult to be scientific about all this if we have to omit significant data from our analytic efforts.)

It is somewhat discouraging to examine the results of one effort made some years ago to isolate three distinct features of liberty. According to Dorothy Fosdick, liberty involves a resentment against constraint; a feeling of capability or competence and concern that the exercise of this competence not be threatened or prevented; and having not only the personal competence but the means to do what one feels competent to do. "Liberty," she tells us, "is held to be endangered or denied when some outside influence prevents the doing of what one desires to do, feels able to do, and has otherwise means for doing."[16]

We appear to make somewhat more progress by referring to the analysis of philosopher Sidney Hook. Hook insists[17] that in asserting any right we are essentially making a claim. But since these claims are claims upon other persons, they become what philosophers call questions of ethics. And rights like life, liberty, and the pursuit of happiness inevitably become incompatible with each other under some circumstances and for some subsets of people. The right to property may threaten the right of liberty, and the rights of some persons may threaten the rights of some others to pursue happiness, and so forth.

---

[16] Dorothy Fosdick, *What Is Liberty?* 2nd ed. (New York: Harper & Row, Publishers, Inc., 1939), pp. 4–5.

[17] Sidney Hook, *The Paradoxes of Freedom* (Berkeley: University of California Press, 1962).

In this connection, an interesting feature of the Constitution of the United States of America is the fact that it is not a handbook for established situations containing a formula for deciding among conflicting or inconsistent rights.

The Constitution contains rules of law—not rules for a game. And as Hook observes, in the case of games like chess (or spelling) "conflicts between rules represents intellectual incoherence—the game cannot be properly played, the word cannot be properly spelled unless there is a higher order rule which resolves the apparent conflict in rules. . . . But in law, conflict of rights and duties confronts us on all sides."[18]

Furthermore, the problem is not solved for a specific set of circumstances by a court decision. The rule formulated by a court deals only with situations demonstrably established in the sense that all relevant features of environmental condition and system state are specified. The court decision simply provides an analytic method for predicting subsequent court responses. But even here, the rule may be changed by a future court or a higher jurisdiction or even by the same court.

When using chess as an illustration (it is comforting to note the large number of other people who like to use chess in their illustrations), Hook is, of course, referring to the rules that define how the game is to be played rather than how to play it effectively. He is, in effect, telling us that in the game of *law*, a pawn may on occasion move like a knight or queen; that on occasion the requirement to protect a castle may supersede the requirement to protect the king; and that all this makes the problem of formulating an adequate principle of play a most difficult one indeed. And now, perhaps, it is possible to understand why men like Proudhon encounter so much difficulty when trying to use a concept like liberty as a tool in system design.

If we define it as a datum of experience, then, as system designers we must insure that whatever the details of the system structure may be at any point in time, they will always meet a specific criterion: permitting participants within the system to experience liberty as a "state of being free," that is, as essentially

---

[18] *Ibid.*, p. 22.

an emotional experience. Every proposed element of structure must be subjected to a test designed to answer the question, "What will the effect of this proposed structure be upon the liberty of each person within the system?" To the extent that individual requirements for liberty change for any reason whatsoever, the details of the system structure must change. Here, the task for the system designer will be to devise new structural configurations that will insure that the goal of liberty is continually achieved.

If, however, we choose to define liberty as a "right," we must at the very outset recognize that the right of liberty for one person may, and in fact unquestionably will, very soon interfere with the right of liberty for another person. We then are faced with the necessity for establishing a priority system that tells us how to resolve such conflicts. To do this we must in effect prescribe a value structure for the system as a whole. Such a value system will prescribe the priorities that are to exist among different goals and the means that may be used to achieve them. The term "right," therefore, can be viewed as a somewhat fuzzy amalgam of ends and means.

If we again ask the question, "What is this thing called liberty and in what sense is it a heuristic?" it seems that our answer must cover at least two distinct points. In the first place, liberty may be viewed as something like a quality-control standard for a system. Assuming that we have a method for determining whether specified persons or groups within the system will experience liberty at any given moment of time, we can design our system so that future structural modifications will occur whenever the waters are lowered in the river of liberty. If we wish to make life somewhat more complex, we may specify an indefinite number of other principles such as justice, equality, and so forth, to which the system will also be sensitive. In this case, however, it will be necessary to provide a specification of priorities among principles that will tell us how much justice is equivalent to a specified amount of liberty, and so on.

The second point to be covered in answering our question involves a determination of the extent to which it is possible for a system to "learn" how to get more or less liberty. But here we come against the same difficulty that plagued us in connection with chess and symbolic logic. What is the major goal toward which the learning is to be directed? Are we to accept the initial priority specifications as the task for the system? This seems to be the reasonable solution, but it provides no mechanism for ongoing adjustments of the priority specifications and introduces the very real difficulty that the system will almost immediately begin to work toward the achievement of outmoded ends.

COMMAND HEURISTICS AND PROHIBITION HEURISTICS

It turns out that liberty is more than simply a random example of a heuristic for purposes of our present discussion. As H. G. Wells put it in describing the ingredients necessary for a "modern utopia," liberty is "the very substance of life. . . . To have free play for one's individuality is, in the modern view, the subjective triumph of existence, as survival in creative work and offspring is its objective triumph."[19]

But the ultimate solution to the problem of liberty is hardly a congenial one by the standards of twentieth-century Western civilization. The creator of the "modern utopia" despairs of ever achieving "perfect" human liberty. This, he tells us, is possible only for a despot who can obtain complete and universal obedience. Although Wells does not use the expression, his image of such a despot is in all essential respects analogous to the image (or caricature?) some system designers envision of a military commander who has been given charge of a modern "command and control" system. The point is that such a despot could, within the constraints of his physical environment or his technology, do exactly what it pleased him to do. Anything short of such a despotism necessitates a compromise among people who assert their freedom of will against each other.

Wells recognizes (as unfortunately many contemporary zealots do not) the fallacy of believing that there is a direct correlation between the existence of law and the limitation of liberty.

---

[19] H. G. Wells, *A Modern Utopia* (London: Chapman & Hall, Ltd., 1905), p. 32.

The designer of the "modern utopia" understands that it is possible, for example, to obtain a net gain in liberty by restricting the common liberty to kill. In his utopia, therefore, two different methods are devised for placing limitations upon liberty. These he calls prohibition ("thou shalt not") and command ("thou shalt"). Of the two, it seems clear that he prefers the former. Prohibiting one specific form of behavior leaves men with an unlimited choice of actions, but compulsion presumably leaves no degrees of freedom whatsoever.

This utopia, consequently, is designed with a heuristic of prohibition as one of its structural features. Specifically this includes prohibitions against killing other people, or assaulting, or threatening them. We may note in passing that Wells was probably much too optimistic in his aspirations for the heuristic of prohibition. Any operational statement of this heuristic necessarily implies a range of actions that are permissible and which can achieve the prohibited end in a given situation. For example, it is not necessary to "kill" a person if one has the power to deny him access to food, shelter, clothing, or medical attention. Bureaucratic arrangements of either a public or private kind can effectively achieve any prohibited end by manipulation of action possibilities. (But we shall discuss this in more detail later.)

Another prohibition found in the "modern utopia" is one against intruding upon the privacy of other persons. This is more in the way of being a temporary prohibition since it is felt that in time more "liberal breeding" will reduce our somewhat excessive requirements for privacy. Nevertheless, the question of privacy and its heuristic raises some very specific problems for the "modern utopia" which receive cursory attention by the designer. In the first place, it is feared that prohibitions against intrusions of privacy will result in a succession of private enclosures which would ultimately place excessive restrictions upon the freedom to travel. Wells finds that this becomes a "quantitative question" which cannot be dealt with by any statement of principle. He assumes that his utopians will deal with the problem through detailed regulations varying with local conditions. Thus, "privacy beyond the house might be made a privilege to be paid for in proportion to the area occupied, and the tax on these licenses of privacy might increase as the square of the area affected. A maximum fraction of private enclosure for each urban and suburban square mile could be fixed. A distinction could be drawn between an absolutely private garden and a garden private and closed only for a day or a couple of days a week and at other times open to the well-behaved public."[20]

What Wells calls a "quantitative question" seems to be based upon a presupposition that the heuristic of prohibition will not apply in any general sense to all situations and locations within the modern utopia. He reserves, for subsequent analysis, the detailed questions about the specific cost of privacy under varying sets of conditions. However, by specifying that privacy beyond the house is to be viewed differently from privacy within the house, he has provided at least a preliminary criterion for making the individual determinations that will later be necessary. By further indicating that the privilege of privacy beyond the house might be taxed in proportion to the area occupied, he has established the basis for a bureaucratic rule or a computer program that could compute the privacy tax under all conditions. The unresolved problem, of course, remains as perhaps the most fundamental one: Is this specific statement of the privacy tax rule a *good* one? Are we indeed prepared to live with it for all areas, all circumstances, and all people? If not, what criteria can we invoke for making modifications? What mechanism is available for changing this rule when it "should" be changed? How can we sense the necessity for a change that "should" be made?

A closer examination of the rule shows the limited nature of its adjustment mechanism. Thus, if we begin with the thought that its objective is to help maximize freedom or liberty for the people living within the "modern utopia," we may wonder about the nature of the possible restrictions that could conceivably limit this liberty.[21]

It is obvious, to begin with, that the physical environment

---

[20] *Ibid.*, p. 42.
[21] Cf. Henry Pratt Fairchild, *The Anatomy of Freedom* (New York: Philosophical Library, 1957).

places many restrictions upon liberty by defining the physical rules of the game. Here are the raw materials of chemical elements and gravity and the first law of thermodynamics and the sun and the moon and all the stars and all the atoms and all their nuclei. And you are not at liberty to go to the moon or to a star without figuring some way of making a spaceship kind of thing out of the chemical elements you find on that earth of yours and no, I'm sorry, you may not borrow materials from Venus or Mars or any of the other planets unless you first figure a way of getting to those places and transporting those materials back to earth. I'm not going to tell you all the rules—you have to figure them out for yourself—I don't care whether you call it science or magic or religion or whatnot—if you can figure it out you may use it, but don't expect any help from me.

And while we're discussing the subject of liberty, remember that you are not at liberty to abuse that body of yours. You must fill it up with acceptable kinds of fuel and you must provide it with liquids of acceptable type (no harsh acids please)— and no matter what you do, it won't go on running forever; and don't let it get too cold or too hot and please remember the oxygen—and watch the air pressure and don't puncture the skin in the wrong places . . . .

And all these restrictions occur before we even mention the restrictions placed upon your liberty by other people. In the first place, they may pass laws that carry penalties of fine, imprisonment, torture, or death. But even if we forget about the laws, they won't let you forget about social ostracism and ridicule, denying you access to the opportunity to earn a living. And if you think you are big enough and strong enough to ignore them, they'll find a way of hurting you through something or someone you love.

With all this in mind, then, let us once again consider the privacy tax rule in the modern utopia. In point of fact, this rule is a legally prescribed *social* procedure designed to help increase liberty. This kind of procedure specifically omits consideration of either the physical environment or the biological characteristics of the men it is trying to help. If we self-consciously address ourselves to the task of devising a procedure that is not restricted to social devices, a much wider spectrum of possibilities appears.

To free the reins on our imagination for a moment, we may, in the first place, think of increasing liberty of privacy by encouraging technological developments in the physical environment. This may ultimately permit residents to live in homes that extend vertically instead of laterally—or to make themselves invisible from prying eyes—or to explore and settle new planets. On the biological level one might think of developing the physical apparatus of human beings either directly or through the use of auxiliary equipment that will allow people to live below the surface of the earth or below the surface of oceans. By modifying the need for bulky food, it might be possible to reduce existing requirements for roads and railways, which reduce the space available for private homes. Again, it might be possible to modify existing needs for travel and new sights by developing elaborate simulations of green fields, fresh breezes, and quaint people within the confines of the individual home. And, even on the social level one might think of developing mechanisms for increasing the social acceptability of completing one's toilet in public—or octracizing explorations beyond the confines of one's own garden—or introducing the custom of wearing blinders while walking outside one's own garden—or using a modification of the emperor's clothing technique by not permitting the sight of other people to register on one's social memory when exploring in the vicinity of the homes of other people.

In short, there are many roads to freedom. The privacy rule outlined by Wells may indeed be one of them, given the framework of the utopia he was describing. But it is only one. And the question remains: Is it a "good" one—that is, an effective one for all situations occurring within the system? If not, what mechanism exists for alerting us to the fact that it should be suspended or changed under a given set of conditions? Will the suggestions we have made, and other suggestions we could make, ever become generated as legitimate items for consideration? If not, how do we make progress—how do we increase the effectiveness of our total arrangements for liberty?

RELATIVIST HEURISTICS

One way of dealing with the problem of finding a universally effective set of heuristics is to abandon the effort and adopt a relativist position, that is, a position that says some are appropriate for one set of conditions and others are appropriate for another set of conditions. This, essentially, is the tack taken by Baron de Montesquieu, who struggled with some of these difficulties early in the eighteenth century.

Montesquieu studied societies of every description, both contemporary and historical, made some empirical observations, and noted some major differences. For example, he noted differences in forms of government. These forms vary in terms of the locus of power. When power is held by all the people, the government is a *democracy*. When power is held by part of the people, it is an *aristocracy*. When a single person holds power, but rules in accordance with some fundamental laws, the government is a *monarchy*. When a single person rules with no restrictions placed upon him other than his own will and caprice, the government is a *despotism*.

Each form of government is characterized by a "principle," which really is a description of the human sentiments necessary for its successful operation. The principle of democracy and aristocracy is *virtue*—love of country or the larger society rather than love of self. If virtue disappears from a democracy or aristocracy, ambition and avarice take over. "Formerly the wealth of individuals constituted the public treasure; but now this has become the patrimony of private persons. The members of the commonwealth riot on the public spoils, and its strength is only the power of a few and the license of the many."[22]

The principle of a monarchy is *honor* or *ambition*—the desire of an individual to promote his own good. If ambition is "pernicious" in a democracy or aristocracy, it is desirable in a monarchy—the point being that people can be motivated to

---

[22] Baron de Montesquieu, *The Spirit of Laws*, rev. ed., trans. Thomas Nugent (New York: The Colonial Press, 1899), I, 21.

great effort with little material reward and with no danger since they can always be controlled. Since the monarchy that Montesquieu considers operates only within the framework of well-defined laws or procedures, virtue is simply not necessary. Its functions are fulfilled through the instrumentality of laws or procedures. Indeed, in a monarchy, Montesquieu tells us, it is difficult for virtue to flourish and it may, in fact, be quite dangerous. Persons located near the apex of the command system set the pattern for the rest of the population:

> Ambition in idleness; meanness mixed with pride; a desire of riches without industry; aversion to the truth; flattery, perfidy, violation of engagements, contempt of civil duties, fear of the prince's virtue, hope from his weakness, but above all, a perpetual ridicule cast upon virtue, are, I think, the characteristics by which most courtiers in all ages and countries have been constantly distinguished. Now it is exceedingly difficult for the leading men of the nation to be knaves and the inferior sort to be honest; for the former to be cheats, and the latter to rest satisfied with being only dupes.[23]

The principle of despotism is *fear*. "Here the immense power of the prince devolves entirely upon those whom he is pleased to intrust with the administration. Persons capable of setting a value upon themselves would be likely to create disturbances. Fear must therefore depress their spirits and extinguish even the least sense of ambition."[24] This form of government requires absolute and undeviating obedience. ". . . when once the prince's will is made known, it ought infallibly to produce its effect. . . . Little does it then avail to plead the sentiments of nature, filial respect, conjugal or parental tenderness, the laws of honor, or want of health; the order is given, and that is sufficient."[25]

Montesquieu's "principles" are not heuristics. They are more or less accurate descriptions of three different kinds of people: virtuous people, ambitious people, and fearful people. In this sense he is analyzing the characteristics of operating units (which we shall discuss in the next chapter). But when he talks about

---

[23] *Ibid.*, p. 24.
[24] *Ibid.*, p. 26.
[25] *Ibid.*, p. 27.

the various forms of government, he is in fact considering alternate heuristics for designing societies. He distinguishes among
these heuristics in terms of the manner in which power is exer-
cised. In contemporary terms, we might say that his heuristics
provide specifications for different decision-making nodes. Montesquieu was really much less euphemistic than his latter-day
counterparts. He was, in point of fact, specifying alternate
heuristics for designing societies, given different assumptions
about the characteristics of the people within the society. If you
have virtuous people, the heuristic of democracy or aristocracy
will work; if you have ambitious people, the heuristic of monarchy will work; if you have fearful people, the heuristic of
despotism will work.

But the relativism of Montesquieu does not end with his
enunciation of form-of-government heuristics as a function of
operating unit characteristics. He extends his relativism to
considerations of the physical environment and, as a result, has
often been condemned if not ridiculed as a "geographical
determinist."

He develops this aspect of his analysis as an extension of
the "general idea" that laws should be appropriate to variations
in the "temper of the mind" and the "passions of the heart." If
these can be shown to vary with climate, then the heuristics of
control and the distribution of power should vary accordingly.

He amasses a great deal of more or less debatable evidence
to support the notion that climate is a major factor in shaping
the forms of human societies. The significant point for our
present purposes is simply that this climatological excursion, far
from being an idiosyncrasy of an otherwise serious thinker, can
in point of fact be seen as a completely consistent extension of
his relativism with respect to principles. His relativism was
based upon an orientation that was strongly empirical. He summarized the differences he found in various climates and then
attempted to relate these differences to variations in attitude and
social practice.

In this sense, Montesquieu was no utopian. He was not bent
on designing a new world so much as he was in understanding

the one in which he lived. This empirical bent constituted both the strength and weakness of Montesquieu's efforts. Devoting his efforts to the task of understanding more thoroughly what *is* or what *was*, he found no method for coming to terms with the problem of what *ought* to be. This, of course, is the driving motivation for utopians in general and seems to constitute in turn their major strength and weakness.

To the extent that one is willing to regard *any* feature of the environment or of a system fixed, the possibilities for creative design are limited. For a true utopian, an empirical finding that climate is a major factor in shaping the potentialities of society would constitute a challenge to find methods for climatological control. For such a utopian, an empirical finding that the possibilities for social organization were limited by the characteristics of operating units would constitute a challenge to modify these characteristics through product engineering, education, selective breeding, or psychological conditioning. The resort to relativistic heuristics is, whether they be based on cultural, climatological, or psychological rigidities, in the final analysis, an admission that some features of systems or environments are unalterably fixed—and this is simply not cricket for bona fide utopians.

INSTRUMENTAL HEURISTICS VS. VALUE HEURISTICS

To the bona fide utopian, empiricism is not enough. He is not content with simply designing systems, organizations, or societies that operate efficiently and effectively—he feels that they must act in ways he would assess as being "good" rather than "bad." He has a more or less well-defined set of values at stake and is, to a considerable extent, a moralist as well as an engineer. Of course, it is quite possible to value efficiency or effectiveness above all other things, and this can, under some circumstances, lead to bizarre or even macabre consequences. For example, the characteristic American impatience with obvious inefficiency in other societies is a well-known phenomenon. Visions of cattle roaming the streets of Indian cities while human populations starve is a favorite illustration used by efficiency worshippers to demonstrate the tragic consequences of non-efficiency ideologies.

But, of course, the possible consequences of a single-minded dedication to efficiency heuristics are seldom carried through to their ultimate implications. For example, the supply of meat is not limitless, even in America. A true efficiency heuristic would require that no possible source of meat be wasted. Obviously, however, untold quantities are indeed unutilized every day. The bodies of dead dogs, cats, or even human beings would undoubtedly provide new sources of supply. But very rapidly the acceptability of some kinds of solution vanishes—for no apparent reason consistent with a rational and instrumental efficiency heuristic. At some point other sets of considerations take over. One way of describing these considerations is to call them situational constraints. They may also be referred to as values. One utopian who struggled with this dilemma of instrumental and value heuristics was a contemporary of Montesquieu —Jean-Jacques Rousseau. One of the major difficulties faced by Rousseau was simply the fact that his heuristics statements did not contain sufficient flexibility to provide useful guidelines under all the conditions his society might face. In short, if his objective was to design a society not merely to operate, but to operate in conformance with a moral code, then his instrumental heuristics were not up to the job.

For example, it is clear that the society he designs will provide "freedom." He tells us that men are born "free" but that they are now "in bondage."[26] If he can find the set of moves that will set them free, he wins. But he continually plays what we might call a "good life" rather than a "freedom" game. The payoff in his game is *not* necessarily freedom; it is something called the good life. Freedom becomes a principle of play. On one hand, it is seen as being purely instrumental—as a way of building a system to provide a good life for its members. On the other hand, it is an end in itself. And problems arise when the instrument and the end provide different prescriptions for action.

No problem exists, however, if one insists upon a rigorously

---

[26] Jean-Jacques Rousseau, *The Social Contract* (Chicago: Henry Regnery Co., 1954), p. 1.

logical and consistent formulation. If the object to be achieved is the good life (appropriately defined), then at each decision point one selects that *action* which is best for the purpose of achieving the good life. Actions may be described along many dimensions. One category may be called freedom. You agree upon a definition of each dimension. You further agree upon a *priority* of actions available from among the several categories. In a specific situation you review this priority scheme to determine whether a given amount of (let us say) freedom is or is not indicated. You then take the indicated action.

In the enactment of such a logical sequence, it is entirely within the range of possibility and, indeed, it is highly probable that your program will in some situations show that the best action to achieve your ultimate objective (that is, the good life) involves some restrictions of freedom for an individual or for many individuals. But if you decide that you do not want to restrict freedom, and still wish to be logical, there is little difficulty in maintaining a different position. You need merely define the game as a freedom rather than a good-life game. But, of course, this is rather difficult to do if you are committed to playing good life. You are in a dilemma and become embroiled in logical inconsistencies. And if there is any one charge that has persisted against Jean-Jacques Rousseau, it is that he was logically inconsistent.

The good life he searches for represents a compromise; it is not a well-defined goal or a set of rules or specifications for individual behavior. Societies become necessary in the first place only because the interests of individuals conflict with one another. But continued existence for the society is possible only when these interests coincide with each other at some point. A society should therefore be run in a manner that will insure the common interest of its members.[27] Rousseau tries to design the kind of government that will be most consistent with the good life of its members. His basic design tools are heuristics like freedom and equality. One that he does not specifically enunciate, but which nevertheless is fundamental to his design in *The Social Contract,*

---

[27] Cf. *ibid.,* p. 33.

might be called "participation." This is the notion that the apparent contradiction between the principle of freedom and the existence of government can be bridged by having all persons subject to the laws of a government participate in the making of those laws. But the heuristic of participation gives him some difficulty. Precisely how does one go about defining participation in a specific situation? One thing is clear: If there are many people who must participate, life becomes difficult. In addition, the force of a particular unit of participation is diminished. This leads to the design solution of many small governments or states rather than one large one. (At one point Rousseau engaged in a little arithmetic exercise to show the existence of something like an inverse correlation between numbers of people who must participate and the amount of freedom.)

Another problem is the frequency of participation. Does everyone participate once a year, once a month, once a day— when? Here, Rousseau decides that participation must be continuous. This implicitly rules out the possibility of a representative democracy, since to delegate the power of participation is to violate the "continuous" part of the participation definition.

A third problem arises when Rousseau attempts to define the results of participation. Logically, everyone who participates must agree to every decision or the entire basis of the principle is subverted. This, however, is manifestly impossible in the world that Rousseau knew. He, therefore, decides that the "majority" will be used to serve as the necessary index of participation. If a majority agrees, then everyone must agree since everyone has participated. But what about the minority? Don't they lose freedom in the process? "Not at all," says Rousseau, in effect, "since everyone has participated, the minority has participated—the majority decision really represents the individual's own will—and therefore the minority must obey or be punished—punishment in this case is something like punishing yourself."

All this may sound inconsistent or even confused. However, it becomes more understandable if we recall the ethical basis of Rousseau's design instruments. His principles serve to make moral sense as well as instrumental sense. The government he has in mind would be incapable of making ruthless, antisocial, or totalitarian kinds of decisions. That is to say, these are not the kind of decisions Rousseau had in mind.

And perhaps this is a clue to some of Rousseau's apparent inconsistencies. He could not be around personally to insure the correctness of all political decisions, he needed some reliable operating units. One way of getting these was to prescribe an educational system that could produce people with Rousseauian properties. These people would take the correct freedom action in a specific situation. The actions necessary in Poland were inevitably quite different from those necessary, let us say, in Corsica. Indeed, his advice to Poland contained in his *Considérations sur le gouvernement de Pologne, sur sa réformation projetée* was quite consistent with the application of his fuzzily defined freedom heuristic. It did not, as has been suggested, reflect a fading of his humanitarian ideal in favor of a "national ideal and with it a markedly conservative temper."[28] Rousseau's heuristic was simply not sufficiently descriptive to communicate the totality of his feelings in the matter.

And this, of course, is one of the difficulties with heuristics or principles. They help provide prescriptions for action in emergent situations, but the prescriptions they provide are characteristically only approximations. As heuristics remain fixed while situations change, they can lead to corruptions and distortions in their original objectives.

Popular controversies over the role of government provide countless illustrations of this dilemma. To a *philosophe* whose perception of government was the tyranny of the French monarchy, "government" represents the enemy of freedom. To the "trust-busters" of the American tradition, industrial "combinations in restraint of trade" constitute enemies of freedom. The formulation of a principle stated at the level of "more" or "less" government is obviously little more than a meaningless semantic exercise. Such a principle can demonstrably result in either more or less freedom, depending upon a variety of other circumstances. Thus, the radicals of the French Revolution and the radical

[28] C. E. Vaughan, ed., *The Political Writings of Jean Jacques Rousseau* (New York: John Wiley & Sons, Inc., 1962), p. 390.

rightists of contemporary America would appear to be strange bedfellows. But, to the extent that they phrase their principles at this level, bedfellows indeed is what they are.

The problem, of course, is not simply one of introducing greater degrees of specificity into the definition of various principles. We have seen how such specificity can result in procedure rigidity and lost games. If, however, we leave the path of specificity and follow one leading from low-level generality to high-level generality to still-higher-level generality, we ultimately arrive at the place called "values."

Now this is a region where many, if not most, scientists feel uncomfortable. It sounds and looks like something outside the science ballpark. If you insist upon going there, you are probably interested in things other than the science game.

What is the science game?

The obvious reply is to insist that science is a game whose objective is "truth." If you find truth, you win; if you fail to find truth, you lose. And for many people in our society—scientists and nonscientists alike—science is the game we should all be playing. We are told by serious thinkers[29] that science is not merely a value prescribing the conduct of the scientist as he works alone, but that it is the overriding value for our entire Western society. If this is the case, a whole series of instrumental heuristics is indicated. They follow naturally and logically from the requirement to do those things which will help uncover truth. They include "independence," "dissent," and even "freedom." A truth-seeker must be independent—and society must protect his independence. He must be original—and society must protect his originality. He may wish to dissent—and society must provide him the opportunity to do so.

It would therefore seem that establishing the value of truth provides a means for achieving the historic American dream. It seems to invite the use of freedom of thought, speech, and individual dignity. But this, unfortunately, is not the case. Indeed, it is possible to invoke the negative of each of the indi-

[29] Cf. Jacob Bronowski, "The Values of Science," New Knowledge in Human Values, ed. Abraham H. Maslow (New York: Harper & Row, Publishers, Inc., 1959), pp. 54–60.

cated instrumental heuristics and to show how necessary this negative is for achieving truth in some situations. For example, restricting the independence of some scientists for a period of time may result in a team "breakthrough" in some scientific endeavor. The heuristic of independence does not provide an infallible guide to freedom. Of course, no heuristic is infallible. In some situations, a heuristic may not even be "good enough." But hopefully, it is better than blind, undirected action based on prejudice or simple randomness. In this connection, we might do well to recall the efforts of such habitual heuristic users as teachers, psychotherapists, and administrators. Even when they fail to achieve hoped-for performance standards, we can sense the existence of "art" or "skill" in an experienced practitioner. Art and skill are words that frequently hide a set of more or less well-developed heuristics. And the daily performance records of such practitioners are typically quite superior to anything that classical science can offer in identical areas (if science is equated with formalist approaches).[30]

Thus the fact that the heuristic of independence does not provide an infallible guide to freedom should not be surprising. Heuristics are not designed for infallibility. Moreover, the heuristic of independence in our discussion was designed to achieve "truth" rather than freedom. And now we can see why confusions between instrumental and value heuristics can complicate some of the critical issues of our times. The dilemma may be stated as follows: Should truth be an end in itself or should truth be a means to an end?

Truth as a means to an end became a necessary antidote to esoteric representations of reality insisted upon by medicine men, soothsayers, pundits, and politicians. The history of empiricism and scientific research is a history of debunked old-wives' tales. These tales served as instrumental heuristics for the ignorant, the superstitious, and representatives of special interests. But when truth alone becomes the end of human existence, one must not be surprised if humanity ultimately emerges as the loser.

---

[30] Cf. Robert Boguslaw, "Situation Analysis and the Problem of Action," *Social Problems*, VIII, No. 3 (Winter 1961), 216.

The spawn of truth is efficiency. Efficiency as an instrumental heuristic leads to more rapid transportation, more automobiles, shoes, solid-state computers—and thermonuclear weapons.

Truth and efficiency are highly effective as instrumental heuristics. But as value heuristics they ignore the prejudices some of us have about the distinctive importance of human beings. There is nothing scientific or efficient about this prejudice; it simply exists. It says that the molecules that make up a human being are somehow more important than the molecules of a tree or a steel cabinet or a factory. This prejudice is something like the prejudice of ethnocentrism. We condemn ethnocentrism because it asserts the importance of one group of human beings over another group of human beings. Humanism simply asserts that humanity is more important than nonhumanity—and this is inconsistent with an orientation that values only truth and efficiency. Within a rigidly defined framework of these values, it is simply not true that the molecules of humanity have priority over other molecules.

Within the framework of systems, organizations, and engineered societies, human beings become operating units. And now we must ask: What are these things called human beings in an operational sense? How do we deal with them in the context of our design specifications?

For this we now turn to an examination of their features in the context of system design—where they take their places alongside of computers, display consoles, and other forms of system operating units.

5

OPERATING UNIT DESIGNS

In explicating the operating unit approach to system design, it seems only fair to warn readers that this seems to be the chosen approach for many technically illiterate, would-be roboteers—and for many technically qualified misanthropes as well.

In an era that delights in analogies between the human organism and its possible electrical or mechanical counterparts—where the expression "giant brains" long has been a popular descriptor for high-speed computing equipment—we must tread a path narrow enough to proceed around a conceptual obstacle course whose hazards range from system engineering and psychological conditioning to adolescent fantasies and science fiction.

Convertibility of Materials—Some Problems

The operating unit approach to system design forces us to think about the difference between the materials of our world, as found in their "natural" state, and the form in which we might *wish* to have them.

Tungsten and silicon are rather uninteresting materials. But Mr. Edison became a national hero because he showed us how to put them together to form a little electric light bulb. No one ever asks tungsten or silicon if they "want" to become a part of an electric light bulb—any more than anyone ever asks turkeys or pumpkins how they feel about becoming components of a Thanksgiving Day dinner. We either ignore the wishes of the turkey and pumpkin or assume that *of course* they want to become connected into our Thanksgiving dinner.

System designers are supposed to think of operating units from the point of view of the *family* at a Thanksgiving dinner rather than from the point of view of the *turkey* or *pumpkin*. At first glance this would seem to create little difficulty as long as the operating units are machines, dumb animals, or vegetables. As a matter of fact, however, things are by no means as simple as our first glance would have us believe.

What does the family require of the turkey? Essentially that it be tender, tasty, attractive, and free from any deterioration. We could, with relatively little difficulty, list the specifications to which our turkey unit must conform. Indeed we might (and do) mass-produce these turkey units to meet the needs of other families on Thanksgiving Day. What can possibly go wrong? Well, our corpulent friends might take umbrage at the calorie count of the stuffing, while our delicate-stomached friends might just "not like turkey." Our wealthy guests might prefer pheasant. Brother might want his turkey "rare." Sister might insist her turkey be "well done." And baby might just be "not hungry."

In system-engineering terms, the problem is simply one of not having adequately determined the "customer's requirements." A careful system engineer, charged with the responsibility of preparing a meal for any given set of guests on a specific occasion, would presumably take great pains to obtain a complete statement of all requirements in advance and insure that his operating units were appropriately tooled to produce specified products. His task would become one of converting the turkey from its natural state to the form that would meet the needs of the customer. However, at some time during his design efforts, he would have to call a halt to changes, and behave as if he knew exactly what the customer requirements in fact were going to be. He would need to assume that no last-minute invitations would be issued, that he could predict the state of baby's appetite, and that he would possess all the relevant facts about the gastronomic predilections and even the religious orientations of his guests. The measure of his ultimate success would be directly related to the accuracy of these predictions.

But we must be careful to avoid confusing a process with a product. The dinner is an *output* of the preparation *process*. It is a *product*. The preparation *process* includes the cook, the stove, and the cooking procedures. The dinner, however, is also an *input* to the diners.

One definition of system design calls it, "The process of creating a system to meet a set of requirements."[1]

Within this framework, one may wish to consider either functions (the jobs the system has to do) or components (the men and pieces of equipment that make up the system). The form to which the materials of the "natural" world are converted by the system—its product—is called the system's output. This may consist of such varied things as refined chemicals, a tool milled to specific tolerances, a radio, a teletype message, a company payroll—or a Thanksgiving dinner. To produce such an output, the system must receive inputs of materials or information.

It is possible to design the system by holding relatively constant either the characteristics of the operating unit or the requirements of the consumer. Thus it is possible to say, "This lawnmower will trim your lawn, but it will cut only that part of the grass one inch or more from the ground." It is also possible to say, "I want the lawn cut to a uniform level of one-half inch above the ground. Use any lawnmower or other instrument that will do that job."

In short, if you use the operating unit approach to system

---

[1] John D. Folley, Jr., and Harold P. VanCott, *Human Factors Methods for Systems Design*, ed. John D. Folley, Jr. (The American Institute of Research under Office of Naval Research, Contract No. Nonr-2700[00], Reproduced by Armed Services Technical Information Agency, Unclassified, AD 232–646, 1960), p. 6.

design, you must begin by answering these kinds of questions: From what vantage point are you going to view the system? Are you going to hold constant the characteristics of the instrument or the requirements of the customer? Are you fundamentally a lawn-mower or a suburbanite?

Consider the problem of operating units in a system to control aircraft landings under conditions of poor visibility. The requirement here is to design a "blind-landing system." Two basic approaches to the problem have been defined: the GCA or ground-controlled approach and the ILS or instrument-landing system. In GCA, the aircraft is observed by one or more ground-based radars. If the position of the aircraft is "improper," oral messages are sent to the aircraft. In ILS, two fan-shaped radio beams are directed along the flight path. One of these is vertical, the other is horizontal. By following the vertical beam, the pilot keeps lined up with the runway. By staying within the horizontal beam, the pilot can keep his plane at the "proper" altitude. The beams actuate two pointers in the cockpit of the plane. By keeping these pointers centered, the pilot will presumably make a safe landing.

In the development of an automatic blind-landing system, a fundamental question to be answered concerns the choice between an automatic GCA or an automatic ILS. Should the fundamental control responsibility (that is, comparing the position of the aircraft with the position of the radio or radio beams and taking corrective action) be placed on the ground or in the air?[2]

Again the problem, in a situation of this sort, is to determine which pair of glasses one will choose to wear. If the designer has pilot vision, he may be tempted to place control in the air; if he has airport vision, he may wish to retain it on the ground; if he has manufacturer or worker vision, he may be influenced to argue for the equipment made at the plant he owns or at which he is employed.

But what, specifically, is it that operating units are called

---

[2] Harry H. Goode and Robert E. Machol, *System Engineering* (New York: McGraw-Hill Book Company, 1957), p. 12.

upon to do? Briefly, they must sense, measure, compare, process, and regulate or handle.[3]

Sensing refers to the job of detecting signals or information in the environment of the system. These signals may include radar returns, dial readings, and so on. The components involved may include such things as a photoelectric cell, a sound-pressure meter, and the human eye, ear, nose, skin, or tongue. If the signals are enlarged or magnified by the system, we are in the presence of an *amplification* function. If some of the signals are suppressed or screened, we have a *filtering* function.

Measuring refers to the job of comparing information that has been sensed with a precalibrated standard or scale. It is possible to *store* measurements in a memory for use at some future time. Components used for this purpose include magnetized tape or disks, punched or marked cards, charged meshes of wire, mechanical relays, or the human brain.

Comparing consists of determining the difference between one measurement and another. Differences are called error signals or simply errors.

Processing consists of combining the available information with a number of different actions to produce some desired decision consequence.

Regulation or handling means acting upon a decision to produce some desired condition or result. Examples of this include: milling a cast to a specified tolerance, controlling the rate of flow of a liquid, and generating a message to another system or to men. The regulation function may be found associated with an actuating function and a power supply that starts and stops handling. It may also be found associated with a *monitoring* function that inspects the quality or quantity of an output.

When a system is conceptualized in these terms, an indispensable portion of its description consists of identifying the *program* it must execute. This is a set of commands given to the system for performing certain operations. When a commander or executive is available he may issue these commands as re-

---

[3] Cf. Folley and VanCott, *op. cit.*, pp. 4–5.

quired. This, in effect, is "real-time" programming. It is also possible, of course, to use some sort of memory to store and issue instructions to the system as they become necessary.[4]

But the concept of "program" as used in this context can be quite deceptive. It seems to imply that when "programmed," the system does only what it is told to do in the program, that is, that the actions it will take are listed in the program. But of course this is scarcely the case. The operating units of the system do what it is possible for them to do. What it is possible for them to do is dependent upon their own structural characteristics, the characteristics of their environment (including other units within the system), and the characteristics of their own internal states at the moment of action. One way of "telling" a radar system to ignore random blips is to issue an instruction to the radar operator. You then have a "programmed" operator. Another way of doing essentially the same thing is to substitute for the human operator a piece of equipment that will "see" only nonrandom blips. The instruction to the piece of equipment does not exist in any usual sense of the term, yet the decision to use the equipment has the same kind of system effect as does the instruction. In one case, the command is contained within a "program"; in the other it is not.

THE STRUCTURE OF OPERATING UNITS

Our concept of "operating unit," it will be observed, seems to include both the ideas contained in "function" and those contained in "component." The "job" a system "has" to perform is essentially a short-range statement of objectives that is deemed valid only under conditions of carefully prescribed environmental states and system states. It presupposes a level of analytic technology that will yield better solutions at the time of design than can be available at the time of action. To the extent that jobs cannot be specified at the time of design, a formal statement of "function" may not be available prior to the action. However,

---

[4] Cf. *ibid.,* p. 5.

the nature of the components actually used in a system implicitly contains a statement of functions in the sense that the components will do what it is possible for them to do at the time of action. Under many conditions of system operation, it may be utterly infeasible or impossible to obtain an advance statement of what the action will be. This will not prevent the action from occurring.

In a competitive situation, knowledge of the idiosyncrasies of an opponent's operating units becomes an invaluable guide to one's own strategy. The use of decoy air traffic to confuse an enemy's air defenses is based upon the knowledge that the enemy depends upon radar equipment that under some sets of circumstances will be unable to distinguish between the radar blips of an aircraft and the blips produced by various "countermeasure" devices.

The radar countermeasure devices themselves can be conceived only after the fundamental inflexible characteristics of radar sensing devices are thoroughly understood. Similarly, counter-countermeasures (responses to countermeasure devices) can be conceived only after the inflexibilities of countermeasure devices become understood.

Understanding the invariant characteristics of operating units is important in other forms of competitive situations—for example, those that occur in connection with the battle of human beings against infectious disease. Here, the operating units involved are parts of the human body. The battle against smallpox provides a case in point. Since ancient times, the people of the Far East had at least one effective weapon to use in fighting smallpox. This weapon consisted of a process that began by introducing pus taken from a smallpox sore into a small wound. A mild case of smallpox developed in the person infected. He usually recovered from the mild attack and retained about as much "immunity" as he would have retained had he recovered from a severe attack of the disease. This process would be called "inoculation" today.

The difficulty with inoculation was that the person inoculated had "true" smallpox and other persons could acquire the disease from him although his own case was relatively mild. The inoculated person could become the focal point of a new epidemic.[5]

Late in the eighteenth century, Edward Jenner became aware of the folk belief that dairymaids who had contracted cowpox from cows they milked did not contract smallpox. Cowpox is similar to smallpox. It produces sores on the udders of cows and the hands of human beings, and these sores resemble smallpox sores. Jenner first vaccinated a boy using matter from the arms of a milkmaid suffering from cowpox. Two months later, he tried to infect the boy with smallpox and found that the boy did not contract the disease. The process that successfully protected the boy against smallpox is called "vaccination." Although the term "vaccination" was originally applied only to the process that used material from lesions of cowpox (*vaccinia*), the term "vaccine" is now employed in a broader sense to include other varieties of inocula used in connection with other kinds of disease.

The point to be made here is simply this: It is quite possible to produce effective immunity against a large number of diseases although the specific mechanism through which this immunity is achieved is not understood. The immunity may be induced through a variety of means, including excreted growth products of bacteria, dead microorganisms, and living infectious microorganisms, the virulence of which has been so reduced or attenuated that no "serious" infection results.[6]

Each of these means is based upon an understanding of the essentially "programmed" responses that will be made by the operating units of the human body. In the language of microbiology, immunity is "specific." A person who recovers from diphtheria becomes immune to diphtheria. He does not necessarily receive immunity to other diseases, such as typhoid fever or whooping cough. But the only reliable method of detecting and measuring many kinds of antibody reactions is to infect

---

[5] Cf. Howard W. Haggard, *Devils, Drugs and Doctors* (New York: Harper & Row, Publishers, Inc., 1929), pp. 222–225.

[6] Martin Frobisher, Jr., *Fundamentals of Microbiology,* 7th ed. (Philadelphia: W. B. Saunders Co., 1962), pp. 336–341.

experimental animals (e.g., mice) and give them doses of the serum to be tested before, after, or simultaneously with an infection. This provides a measure of the protective or neutralizing power "regardless of whether this power depends on agglutinins, cytolysins or some still-undiscovered antibody."[7]

Knowing characteristics of operating units within the human body is sufficient for medical practitioners and medical researchers. If medical men were obliged to defer preventive measures against such diseases as smallpox, typhoid, cholera, yellow fever, and the like until it was possible to describe the mechanism that produces antibodies, Western civilization might very well not now exist, at least in its present form.

But it is simply not true that immunity is obtained as a result of any specific "program" of instructions to the human body (unless, of course, we wish to invoke metaphysical or theological issues, which are beyond the scope of this book). The characteristics of the human operating unit allow it to generate immunities against many diseases *without* the use of inoculations of any sort. It is not the inoculations that make the operating units and immunity possible, but rather the characteristics of the operating units that make the development of inoculation and vaccinations possible. In this sense, the use of these measures represents a clever example of simulation technology; by using a mild form of disease to simulate a more severe form, the body's operating units are induced to behave in some wished-for manner, that is, to produce antibodies.

In short, it is clear that the "job specifications" of the human operating unit relative to the prevention of disease do *not* include a specific statement of each form of every microbe against which appropriate antibodies must be generated. The body must "know" what it will do under every possible set of circumstances. Faced with an infinity of different situations, it will do what its structural characteristics allow it to do, but it is by no means necessary that this knowledge be available in a published "program" in order for the unit to operate effectively. The program may be "built into the body," as it is "built into equipment," but in

---

[7] *Ibid.*, p. 331.

neither case is it always possible to specify exactly what it contains. And this specification is clearly not an indispensable prerequisite for system operation or design. In short, we may and do use operating units without either knowing the details of their structure, or being able to specify what these details should be.

Design Phases

Precisely how does one go about designing a system using the operating unit approach? In contemporary engineering circles, this approach is a familiar one. It is the basic methodology used to design many forms of "control systems."

A control system is "an integrated complex of devices that governs or regulates a process or an operation."[8] Examples include: numerically controlled milling machines, automatic electronic assembly lines, engine-block production lines, program-controlled lathes, automatic inspection and quality control devices, material-handling automata, packaging and bottling machines, dial telephone systems, automatic railroad freight-sorting yards, pipeline controls, air traffic control systems, autopilot and landing devices, chemical plants, nuclear controls, petroleum refineries, distilleries, fire control systems, iron-lung regulators, and synthetic human organs (for example, heart and kidney).

The first task involved in designing such a system is to *formulate the design problem*.[9] The "problem" might involve performing a fixed set of operations required in a bottling machine, maintaining a sequence of specified conditions in a chemical process, or adapting to a range of changing circumstances. The language used to specify the problem is couched in terms of quantitative data about inputs, outputs, performance requirements, the state of the environment, cost, and time schedules. It is important to insure that the problem is not expanded to inefficient limits, or subjected to "excessively stringent specifi-

---

[8] M. E. Connelly, "System Design," *Handbook of Automation, Computation and Control*, ed. Simon Ramo, Eugene M. Grabbe, and Dean E. Woolridge (New York: John Wiley & Sons, Inc., 1961), III, 1–01.

[9] *Ibid.*, p. 1–04.

cations in the hope that all possible contingencies will be adequately covered."[10] "Partial treatment" of a problem can result in such outcomes as the design of an air traffic control system to coordinate the arrival of 200 aircraft an hour into an area, while the landing system can handle no more than 20 planes per hour.

After the problem has been formulated, an outline of *system functions* is prepared. This consists of an outline of the operations necessary to cope with the problem. The organization of operations follows one of three characteristic patterns. The first of these, called "simple sequence control," involves nothing more than a simple sequence of specified steps. Depending upon the kind of "control logic" utilized, it may be possible to control complex operations by using switching circuits to intervene at various positions or times. This can readily be extended to include an ability to choose between alternate modes of operation depending upon circumstances, for example, ". . . if condition A *or* condition B exists *and* if condition C also exists, then response D will be activated. However, if condition A *or* condition B exists *and* condition C does *not* exist, then response E will be activated."[11]

A second method for controlling operations is called "programmed control." This involves the use of a program of instructions. The functions of the system can be changed by simply changing the program. A third method called "continuous control" employs a cybernetic type of arrangement in which the operations are continuously and automatically adjusted to the state of the process or operation being controlled. Examples of this include a device like an autopilot, whose function it is to detect deviations from some desired state in an aircraft's location and progress and reduce these deviations to zero.[12]

In each of these cases, it will be noted, the method used to accomplish the objective involves the insertion of a piece of equipment with the appropriate characteristics. Varied instructions are possible through the use of circuitry that rapidly

---

10 *Ibid.*, p. 1–05.
11 *Ibid.*, p. 1–07.
12 *Ibid.*, p. 1–09.

changes some clearly definable structural characteristic of the operating unit equipment.

Following the preparation of an outline of operations, a *detailed system design* is prepared. This may be accomplished at several different levels of generality, but usually involves the preparation of system block diagrams. These block diagrams are used to "divide the functions of the system into logical subsidiary operations, to indicate the flow of information throughout the system, or to represent the system dynamics schematically."[13]

It is at this stage that a wide variety of design decisions must be made. These include such things as determinations about whether the system will be manual, automatic, semiautomatic; what data will be selected for various forms of representation; whether the system components will be electronic devices, mechanical devices, hydraulic devices; whether the input-output devices used will be manual, typewriter, plugboard, punched tape, magnetic tape, punched cards, film, magnetic disks, or cathode ray tubes. If a digital computer is to be used, decisions must be made about the memory capacity of the computer, the length of words that can be processed, whether fixed- or floating-point arithmetic will be used, the nature of the standard program instructions that will be available, and so on.

If the major units of the system have been fixed, the remaining units must be selected for compatibility; for example, if the aircraft to be used with a given autopilot design is fixed, the structural characteristics of the autopilot must be consistent with the dynamics of this particular aircraft.[14]

A "dynamic analysis" is then performed to help determine realistic design criteria for the various units of the system. The interactions of all units may be simulated on a computer, or selected aspects may be subjected to mathematical analysis. In either case, a range of situations is selected and anticipated system performance in these situations is examined. "The situations chosen may represent the worst cases that the system is

---

[13] *Ibid.*, p. 1–11.
[14] *Ibid.*, p. 1–14.

expected to encounter, or may represent a statistical sample of representative cases."[15]

Following the preparation of a detailed system design, a *detailed unit design* is begun. In many respects the procedure used here is similar to that used in the preceding phase. It begins with the construction of a block diagram to show the basic techniques by which the operation of a unit is to be performed. The principal components are then selected. This is characteristically accomplished after a survey of commercially available components has been conducted and possibly after some comparison testing of these components in a laboratory.[16]

The *final design* stage is preceded by a series of unit and system tests in the laboratory or in a pilot plant operation. "Every experienced engineer is acquainted with the utter perversity of nature. . . . Almost inevitably, a host of shortcomings appears in the course of these tests, many of which originate in the incompatibilities and interactions between units of the system."[17]

The final system must be "thoroughly checked for performance under a variety of conditions, and any new deficiencies must be corrected. The ultimate user will most likely require a field test or demonstration of the system before acceptance, as well as complete operating and maintenance manuals, schematics and parts lists."[18]

In the case of complex systems, "field service personnel may remain with the unit for months after delivery for maintenance purposes, additional debugging and training of customer personnel. Some control systems are purchased with provisions for permanent field service."[19]

The reiterative characteristics of this final design stage illustrate perhaps as eloquently as any research findings might the extent to which these control systems consist of operating units whose structural characteristics are not completely understood. The final selection and tooling of system components

[15] *Ibid.*, p. 1–18.
[16] *Ibid.*, pp. 1–21 to 1–23.
[17] *Ibid.*, p. 1–24.
[18] *Ibid.*, p. 1–25.
[19] *Ibid.*, pp. 1–25 to 1–26.

becomes a problem whose ultimate solution is empirical and relative to the environmental conditions actually encountered in test or real-life operations. This, of course, is the case whether the operating units happen to be hardware or human. The control systems we have been discussing may or may not use human operating units as components. It seems clear, however, that the steps reviewed are stated in a form that is heavily indebted to the tradition of hardware engineering—the tradition that has made its most notable achievements in the control of operating units composed of such ingredients as metal, electricity, chemicals, and the like. What special considerations are involved in the use of human operating units?

The Use of Human Operating Units—
A Digression

Our immediate concern, let us remember, is the explication of the operating unit approach to system design, no matter *what* materials are used. We must take care to prevent this discussion from degenerating into a single-sided analysis of the complex characteristics of one type of system material: namely, human beings.

What we need is an inventory of the ways in which human behavior can be controlled, and a description of some instruments that will help us achieve control. If this provides us sufficient "handles" on human materials so that we can think of them as one thinks of metal parts, electric power, or chemical reactions, then we have succeeded in placing human materials on the same footing as any other materials and can proceed with our problems of system design. Once we have equated all possible materials, one simply checks the catalogue for the price, operating characteristics, and reliability of this material and plugs it in where indicated. For an engineer or industrial designer, these are precisely the terms upon which human beings must be considered. This is not, of course, to imply that engineers are cruel, heartless, or inhuman. They are, as they would put it, "simply trying to do a job." It is, they would assert, "inhuman" to insist that human beings perform duties that can be passed on to nonhuman materials. This frees human beings for golf, philosophy, music, and business deals.

It is, of course, possible to control many aspects of human behavior. The technology of Madison Avenue and related centers has become notorious for its ability to shape consumer habits and political opinion. It is possible, within limits, to establish conditions in a work group that will facilitate increased productivity, originality, and morale. It is possible to predict, again within limits, which members of an organization will be troublesome and/or delinquent. It is possible to influence moods, attitudes, and behaviors through drugs; to produce hallucinations in normal individuals through establishing appropriate conditions; to disintegrate a man's personality structure, dissolve his self-confidence, destroy his concept of himself and make him completely dependent upon another.[20]

It has been suggested that there are at least five instruments[21] through which this control can be achieved:

1. *Emotional Conditioning.* For example, the *Brave New World* process of permanently dissuading certain inferior types of citizens from wasting time on books and the beauties of nature. Babies are given electric shocks as they are about to touch books and flowers. The converse of this is employed in advertising displays showing a product used by or associated with pretty girls or admired public figures.

2. *Motivational Controls.* For example, starving whole populations so that food may be used to reinforce those who support the government; creating art, literature, movies, or comic books to appeal to persons with sadistic tendencies; or designing an automobile so that riding in it provides a measure of sexual experience.

---

[20] Cf. Carl R. Rogers, "Implications of Recent Advances in Prediction and Control of Behavior," *Teacher's College Record,* LVII (February 1956), 316–319.

[21] Cf. B. F. Skinner, "The Control of Human Behavior," *Cumulative Record* (New York: Appleton-Century-Crofts, 1959), pp. 19–21.

3. *Positive Reinforcement.* Wages, bribes, tips, or personal attention as used by Dale Carnegie, Lord Chesterfield, and some clinical psychologists.

4. *Drugs.* Using liquor or tranquilizers. "In the not-too-distant future, the motivational and emotional conditions of normal daily life will probably be maintained in any desired state through the use of drugs."[22]

5. *Knowledge of the Individual.* Using information about an individual to control him, for example, eavesdropping, employing spies and informers, opening mail, wiretapping, using projective tests in psychology, or the political "trial balloon."

But all these are, of course, obvious and even crude. It is not necessary to starve a population to make its members do the only work available to earn a livelihood. It is not necessary to control a human being through bribes, blackmail, or drugs, when it is possible to filter his access to the environment in which he must eat, drink, think, love, and live.

There are, however, many disadvantages in the use of human operating units. They are somewhat fragile; they are subject to fatigue, obsolescence, disease, and death; they are frequently stupid, unreliable, and limited in memory capacity. But beyond all this, they sometimes seek to design their own system circuitry. This, in a material, is unforgivable. Any system utilizing them must devise appropriate safeguards.

Some Further Design Considerations

As we have previously noted in Chapter I, B. F. Skinner's fictional utopia, *Walden Two*, provides an illustration of a system designed essentially along the lines of the operating unit approach. Skinner, however, is not simply a utopian; he also happens to be a distinguished psychologist. His approach to the design of control systems is by no means simple scientific window dressing; it proceeds from a deeply humanitarian orientation.

---

[22] *Ibid.,* p. 20.

Yet his conclusions have left many of his fellow psychologists deeply uneasy.

Carl R. Rogers is one of these. Rogers, in his classic debate with Skinner,[23] describes the "usual" concept of human behavior control as consisting of five elements:

1. Decide about goals. Examples of this include the "undesirable" decision to aggrandize power as described in George Orwell's *1984*, and the "desirable" decision suggested by Skinner: namely, "let men be happy, informed, skillful, well behaved and productive."
2. Use the methods of science to discover the means to the ends selected.
3. Establish the conditions and use the methods, having first obtained the power to do so.
4. Expose individuals to the prescribed conditions.
5. Establish social organization to continue to produce the types of behavior that have been valued.

It will be observed that this formulation has marked similarities to M. E. Connelly's description (summarized earlier in this chapter) of the major steps in the design process as seen by a system engineer. An interesting shift of emphasis is apparent, however. The "decision about goals," that Rogers lists is quite similar to Connelly's "formulation of the design problem." However, much of Connelly's exposition is devoted to an explication of the "methods of science" through which these goals are to be achieved. He simply *assumes* the existence of a "social organization to produce the types of behavior which have been valued," and the existence of the necessary "power" to implement the design decisions. Rogers is obviously quite concerned about the nature of the organization as well as the process of power allocation.

Rogers sees the utopia of Skinner's *Walden Two* as fundamentally similar to George Orwell's *1984*. In both cases, the power to control is retained by some person or group. The results

---

[23] Carl R. Rogers and B. F. Skinner, "Some Issues Concerning the Control of Human Behavior," *Science,* CXXIV (November 1956), 1057–1065.

of this control include elimination of the notion of human freedom, responsibility for choice, and the worth of the human
individual.[24]

Skinner, however, strenuously objects to the notion that
Walden Two and *1984* have anything in common. "The book
1984," he tells us, "is a picture of immediate aversive control for
vicious selfish purposes. The founder of *Walden Two*, on the
other hand, has built a community in which neither he nor any
other person exerts any *current* control. His achievement lay in
his original *plan*. . . ."[25]

It should be observed that perhaps the core of this controversy is a question that Rogers raises but which both Skinner
and our friends, the system engineers, assume as a "given." The
question is simply one of the relationship between the source of
control in a system and the system mechanisms required to maintain the control—that is, what characteristics must the operating
units of a system possess in order to insure that they will be
responsive to commands issued from a control point?

As a matter of fact, this question is *not* usually ignored by
system engineers. A computer system is characterized by input
components which accept punched cards, magnetic tapes, and
the like without question. The person or group who wishes to
control this system must have access to the kinds of cards and
tapes that will be acceptable to the input components. If these
components become "defective" and refuse to accept a standard
card or tape input, the unit must be "repaired."

Now Skinner, in *Walden Two*, is describing a system that
has little need for "repair." Orwell, in *1984*, describes a much
less reliable system. Most of the novel's drama stems from accounts of system repairmen at work, repairing and eliminating
defective operating units. However, these operating units (the
defective ones) happen to be people, and our sense of the
fitness of things rebels at the notion of this kind of repair. Not
that we are unfamiliar with the notion of repair of human beings.
Our most revered human repairmen are called physicians,
surgeons, dentists, and so forth, but we place a different set of

[24] Carl R. Rogers, *ibid.*, p. 1062.
[25] B. F. Skinner, *ibid.*, p. 1065.

values upon the kind of repair work they do. Prolongation of life is a highly prized value of our tradition and has been so since at least the days of the ancient Hebrews. So, when the henchmen of Big Brother in Orwell's *1984* cause citizens to disappear, presumably because they have been destroyed, we are shocked. When a defective nonhuman (that is, a physical operating unit) is replaced because of its faulty operation, we applaud the system engineer or mechanic.

In *Walden Two,* as we have indicated, the need for repairmen seems to be considerably less than in *1984.* (It is possible that the need for repairmen may be equivalent in both societies. Skinner, however, is promoting an operating unit approach, so he focuses on its virtues. Orwell is attacking the approach, so he focuses on its weaknesses.)

Skinner's hero, Frazier, is essentially a scientist rather than a power-hungry despot. He is concerned with understanding the basic operation of the human organism. "What are the basic psychological characteristics, if any, and the possibility of modifying them and creating others?" he asks. Furthermore, "What are the techniques, the engineering practices, which will shape the behavior of all members of a group so that they will function smoothly for the benefit of all?"[26]

This, of course, is essentially the same question that Big Brother had to have answered. However, his solution to the design problem—his system as described in *1984*—strikes us as being considerably less efficient than Frazier's in *Walden Two.* In both systems, occasional lapses occur in the effectiveness of operating units. In *1984,* these lapses are corrected through a large, expensive organization of repairmen who use a variety of repair techniques. These range from direct measures, such as the ruthless destruction of defective parts, through such intermediate techniques as psychological conditioning, down to such subtleties as altering the collective memory of the systems by changing records and enforcing consistency of operating unit response. The development of "Newspeak," a language whose structure and vocabulary were intended to make deviant thought

---

[26] B. F. Skinner, *Walden Two* (New York: The Macmillan Company, 1948), p. 145.

patterns impossible, is a technique for insuring consistency of operating unit response.

It seems clear that Frazier does not object to direct controls on occasion, especially if the objects of that control are not human beings. In *Walden Two*, a flock of sheep is used to keep the lawn cropped. The sheep are moved by utilizing a portable electric fence. The sheep learn to avoid the fence and ultimately a piece of string is substituted for the electric fence. Here, the only defective units that become apparent consist of the new baby lambs who have not been conditioned by the electricity. But Frazier takes a relaxed attitude about them. "They stray," he concedes, "but they cause no trouble and soon learn to keep with the flock."[27] Indeed, most of the sheep have never actually been shocked by the electric fence; it has become traditional among them to avoid the string.

In *Walden Two*, considerable effort is devoted to the construction of operating units. If the adult operating unit was born within the boundaries of *Walden Two*, he has gone through the procedures of childhood conditioning. Since self-control is viewed as a useful quality for human operating units to possess, all children undergo a series of lessons designed to give them the necessary attributes. Upon returning from a long walk, tired and hungry, each child is required to stand before a bowl of steaming soup for five minutes without touching it. Any groaning or complaining constitutes a wrong answer. Presumably, anyone who disobediently reached for a bowl and downed it would flunk the course. However, it is not made completely clear why passing the course should matter greatly to children who are less than six years of age.

If such behavior became widespread, we might expect Frazier to devise techniques for simply denying the children accessibility to the soup—through the use of glass covers or some other obstacle. In *1984* we might expect severe punishment to follow any similar infraction of rules. In both cases, the goal is clear: to tool the human operating units so that their behavior conforms to some predetermined set of specifications.

---

[27] *Ibid.*, p. 14.

Another possible approach to the problem of tooling operating units to necessary specifications has only rarely been considered seriously. This approach consists of increasing the capabilities of "dumb" animals, rather than helping along human babies or inventing mechanical and electronic "robots." George Orwell's *Animal Farm*, subtitled "A Fairy Story," explores some possibilities involved in such "zoomorphism."[28]

The thesis upon which this "fairy story" is predicated is quite simple: The animals living on the farm of Mr. Jones are seen to have qualities characteristically not possessed by dumb animals. Their intelligence has increased to the point where they can discuss the tyranny of Mr. Jones and make plans to overthrow his regime. If we ignore such minor considerations as the difficulty encountered by four-legged animals in using farm equipment designed for two-legged men, we can soon forget the difference between human beings and the beasts. Orwell does not tell us how to change animals—he simply describes a system in which they, in fact, have become changed. It would seem that, with the use of such techniques as selective breeding and artificial modification of gene structure, the road leading to zoomorphism is no more difficult than the one leading to construction of electronic and mechanical robots. An operating unit is an operating unit is an operating unit.

The novelist John Hersey is another opponent of the operating unit approach when the units are human beings. He has described in considerable detail a process for increasing the intelligence quotient of human subjects and devoting that intelligence exclusively to the system task at hand. This process, as outlined by his character, Mr. Wissey Jones, in *The Child Buyer*, consists of five stages. The process begins with a period of complete isolation for the human subject, who has been carefully selected on the basis of having a "high IQ." During this period his memory is cleared of all pre-existing experience, knowledge, and education. During the second period, he is educated and conditioned to solve problems for the United Lymphomilloid Company, his employer. In the third period, his mind is fed an

---

[28] George Orwell, *Animal Farm* (New York: The New American Library of World Literature, Inc., 1956).

enormous quantity of data. In the fourth period, he undergoes major surgery which "ties off" all five senses; he is left with just enough sense of touch to permit him to carry on his bodily functions and "write" on a stenographic machine called the Simplomat Recorder. In the fifth and final stage, he solves incredibly difficult problems for United Lymphomilloid.[29]

One consequence of this United Lymphomilloid method was to produce operating units whose intelligence quotients checked out at over the 1000 level. Prior to the use of this method, it is noted, IQ's as high as 200 had been attained by only a handful of geniuses such as Goethe, Pascal, and John Stuart Mill.[30]

Since *The Child Buyer* is a novel, we may forgive Hersey some of his imaginative flights. Unfortunately, however, the underlying view of intelligence that his tale satirizes is actually held by many of our most serious-minded new utopians. Efforts to increase the "intelligence" of nonhuman operating units through "automation" or the manufacture of "robots" often stem from precisely this kind of fuzzy conceptual premise. Some of these efforts begin by viewing intelligence as a sort of disembodied gadget used to do things other gadgets can't do. A third-degree-equation gadget does something a second-degree gadget can't do; a second-degree-equation gadget does something a first-degree-equation gadget can't do, and so on.

But in every case the gadgets have their tasks carefully defined for them. They are told what behavior is legitimate, and their environments are carefully established. Efforts by these operating units to change their environments and goals would be condemned as gadget malfunctioning rather that applauded as manifestations of intelligent behavior.

The extravagant "IQ" levels discussed in *The Child Buyer* refer to something other than "intelligence." Clearly, any operating unit possessing bona fide intelligence of an order describable as "over 1000" would very rapidly find a way to terminate its employment with United Lymphomilloid—given the employment conditions described in the novel.

---

[29] John Hersey, *The Child Buyer* (New York: Bantam Books, Inc., 1961), pp. 181–185.
[30] *Ibid.*, p. 185.

The operating unit designs we have been discussing utilize what we should probably call instinctive, rather than intelligent, behavior. Normally, instincts refer to fixed behavior patterns that are not subject to modification by the environment, either through learning or conditioning. They are not simple reflexes but inherited stimulus-response chains. Psychologists usually distinguish them from habits, which *can* be modified or even forgotten. (Also, if a habit is interrupted, the behavior will be resumed where it left off; if an instinct is interrupted, the behavior will start all over again.) But, it is useful, for some purposes, to consider both habits and instincts under the single heading of instinctive behavior.[31] It is in this sense that the inhabitants of *Walden Two*, the Oceanians of *1984*, and the components of contemporary, system-engineered systems are all behaving instinctively rather than intelligently.

This, of course, is not necessarily bad—it is simply incomplete. When we say that an operating unit is behaving instinctively, we are simply asserting that it is behaving in a manner that is fixed by its structure. A carburetor or a spark plug in an automobile does what it is able to do and what it must do. Change the car or the fuel or the amount of moisture in the immediate environment, and these operating units will continue to do what it is possible for them to do under the circumstances. No one wants an "intelligent" carburetor. A truly intelligent carburetor might decide to occupy the driver's seat. What we require of a carburetor is that it be *reliable*. We don't want it to decide suddenly that a carburetor's life is not a happy one—that it would prefer to be a spark plug or condenser as a way of broadening its horizons.

A "good" or "effective" operating unit is one that has "adjusted" to its environment. It accepts the environmental conditions postulated by its system designer as a "given," and it does what its structure permits it to do. The central difficulty that arises lies in the definition of "environment." A "bad" thermonuclear weapon would be one that exploded before some "responsible" human being "pressed the button," or because it

<hr>

[31] Claire Russell and W. M. S. Russell, *A New Approach to Human Behavior* (Boston: Little, Brown & Co., 1961), p. 50.

simply "felt" like exploding. Human beings generally don't want "intelligent" thermonuclear weapons. But the man who presses the button is part of the environment of the weapon. The factors that lead to the button's being pressed are equally part of this environment. The social, economic, emotional, political, or other issues that help determine whether the button will be pressed are all part of the bomb's environment. Do you design a bomb to be detonated with one finger, two fingers, or two hundred million fingers? This is all part of the system design problem when you design systems with the operating unit approach.

The safest procedure is to build a system with operating units resembling Mr. Zero of Elmer L. Rice's *The Adding Machine*.[32] Whether serving as a Roman galley slave, a serf, or an American bookkeeper about to be displaced by an adding machine, Mr. Zero is completely reliable, noninnovative, and safe. The designer of his universe is undoubtedly a shrewd, cost-conscious engineer. He collects used souls in a sort of heavenly dry-dock, cleans and repairs them, and ships them out to occupy new bodies. For purposes of minimizing costs and maximizing efficiency within a predictible cosmos, this is obviously a highly intelligent solution. There is, of course, no requirement for Mr. Zero to be intelligent; he remains eternally a Zero.

This is not to imply that Mr. Zero is incapable of independent action. He can learn to speak, read, write, hold a job, raise a family, quarrel with his wife, and discuss politics. It is not necessary to program his daily activities; they will fall well within specified tolerances. His purpose in the scheme of things is simply to be himself. One might, of course, find it interesting to speculate about the long-range objectives of his designer (which are not specified)—but that, as our new utopians might say, is another problem.

In any event, his designer seems to be faced with a constantly changing universe. He deals with this dynamic universe by using dependable operating units like Mr. Zero. In doing so, he is confronted with the same issue that other operating unit

---

[32] Elmer L. Rice, *The Adding Machine* (New York: Samuel French, Inc.), 1922.

system designers must resolve: How much self-determination should these operating units be allowed to possess?

In science fiction accounts of robot manufacture and utilization, specifications are usually prescribed in terms of structural invariants. Thus, the robots are so constructed that the requirement to protect human beings always supersedes every other possible instruction. The robot obeys orders of human beings except when these orders involve possible violations of its primary commandment. Protecting its own existence becomes a third-order priority. Fascinating drama is to be found emerging from the basic conflict between the necessity to provide means for independent robot action and the necessity for insuring ultimate designer control.[33] Much of this drama centers about the devious maneuvers used by robots to accomplish their assigned tasks. From the perspective of the human actors involved, specific actions taken by the robots seem to constitute violations of fundamental robot commandments.

If a robot is allowed too much independent action, it may begin to assert the pre-eminence of its own goals over those of its designer. It is then a "rebel" and its behavior is appropriately referred to as a "revolt."

But how "intelligent" must an operating unit be before it is able to revolt? Or conversely, how "stupid" must the designer insist that his operating unit be to insure reliable system performance? And, from the perspective of the operating unit, what are the necessary and sufficient conditions for effective rebellion?

For Albert Camus, a rebel is essentially an operating unit with established internal limits. It has more or less suddenly decided that the system designer has begun to infringe upon the integrity, not only of the operating unit itself, but of operating units in general. Rebellion, Camus insists, is not fundamentally an egoistic act. The rebel demands respect for himself, but only to the extent that he identifies himself with a natural community.[34] In this sense, it is possible to understand the "human" as

[33] Cf. Isaac Asimov, *I, Robot* (New York: Doubleday & Company, Inc., 1956).

[34] Albert Camus, *The Rebel* (New York: Vintage Books, 1958), p. 16.

opposed to the exclusively "functional" quality of operating units. "Rebellion . . . reveals the part of man which must always be defended."[35] It is thus rebellion which ultimately defines the scope of his humanness.

System designs with fixed, unalterable goals inevitably assign second-level or lower priorities to such things as operating unit integrity or operating unit values. If a revolt occurs without changing the priority system, it will result in a simple substitution of one set of operating units for another, but the basic difficulty will remain. This, essentially, is the conclusion at which Camus arrives after his survey of rebel and revolt phenomena. He is, of course, inveighing against totalitarian societies which begin with revolt and end in tyranny.

It might, therefore, seem that one could well stand Camus on his head and insist that, instead of including goals within the total system design, they ought to be completely restricted to the operating unit level. This leads directly to the bizarre form of anarchic individualism to be found, for example, in the novels of Ayn Rand.[36] The very existence of society seems to infuriate the heroes of these novels. After some second thoughts it is conceded that perhaps there is a limited role to be found for government: protecting man from physical violence. But what is "violence?" Is it slapping someone's face? or twisting his arm? or denying him access to raw materials he needs for a livelihood? or inducing him to buy worthless stocks? or adulterating the food, beverage, or medicine you sell him? None of this is made clear, and we are left with the prospect of a world inhabited by strong, silent, paranoid giants—vicious caricatures of the human spirit—each of whom sees the universe and everything in it exclusively in terms of his own whims.

Perhaps the authentic rebels of mid-twentieth-century western civilization, however, are neither the politically sensitive rebels of Camus nor these paranoid economic men of Ayn Rand. They may very well prove to be the marijuana-smoking, poetry-

---

[35] *Ibid.*, p. 19.
[36] G. Ayn Rand, *Atlas Shrugged* (New York: Random House, 1959).

writing, jazz-listening "hipsters" of the "beat" generation. The hipster rebels against a society which he can define as "rational but no longer sane,"[37] but this insanity cannot be defined in customary clinical terms. It stems from fundamental differences about what is important. The hipster and his fellow beats are disillusioned and alienated from civilization's primary thrust, which insists upon using human beings exclusively as operating units in the contemporary pushbutton utopias. This demands a sacrifice of individual "spontaneity," freedom of action, and personal integrity. The use of fantasy-inducing drugs or music, and poetry of escape, represents an alternative to space technology for those who want to "get out of this world."

The beats are technically illiterate, but they are not Ayn Rand's would-be Roboteers of the human spirit. They are not evangelistic misanthropes. Their technology is the technology of environmental escape; their utopian dream is populated with cloud-cushioned flocks of free-floating operating units.

Unfortunately, utopias consisting of infinitely free-floating or self-sufficient operating units are every bit as unrealistic as formalist utopias made by whiz kids or other highly intelligent system designers. The dilemma is not resolved by insisting that human beings withdraw from the system race any more than it is by insisting that systems must withdraw from the human race. Decisions made by operating units acting either independently or as direct agents of a designer affect human populations directly through their impact upon the conditions of human existence. It is not only the human beings serving as operating units who are affected, but those outside the system as well. The critical point is not the location of people with respect to the system, but the nature of the decisions made and the actions taken which affect their destinies.

In this context, discussions about whether man should be adjusted to physical equipment or vice versa become gigantic non sequiturs. When the operating units are not simply tools but machines in varying states of operating independence, it is men

---

[37] David McReynolds, "Hipsters Unleashed" in *The Beats*, ed. Seymour Krim (Greenwich, Conn.: Fawcett Publications, Inc., 1960), p. 209.

who must adjust. Hannah Arendt has observed, "Even the most primitive tool remains a servant unable to guide or replace the hand. Even the most primitive machine guides the body's labor and eventually replaces it altogether."[38]

But this, of course, is a profound understatement. The replacement is much more than a simple substitution of machine for human labor. It is becoming increasingly more obvious that a surrender of decision-making prerogatives is involved. The values of human populations increasingly become excluded from the dialogue between operating units and their environments. Operating units requirements become both the short-run and long-range goals of human populations. The information necessary to understand operating unit characteristics becomes the content of educational programs; operating unit characteristics shape society's demand for natural resources, economic arrangements, philosophical orientations, and family life. This is the strength and the tragedy of human beings in search of systems within which they can assume their roles as operating units.

---

[38] Hannah Arendt, *The Human Condition* (New York: Doubleday & Company, Inc., 1958), p. 129.

6

AD HOC DESIGNS

Having examined approaches to system design that require commitments to models, heuristics, or operating units, we now turn to an approach that is committed to none of these. The ad hoc approach, as we have previously indicated, can be characterized on the one hand by an absence of such commitments, and on the other hand by an overshadowing concern with present reality or the "here and now."

But the central criticism directed at designers of utopian systems throughout the ages consists of the charge that they have been "visionary," "impractical," and "divorced from reality." Indeed, despite Mannheim's efforts to use the word "utopian" to refer only to those ideas that *change* existing states of affairs, the aura of impracticability continues to enshroud the idea of utopia and shield it from the serious scrutiny of men of affairs.

The ad hoc approach to system design, therefore, seems to create a contradiction when it appears in a discussion of utopian efforts. The ad hoc approach begins with a view of present reality —how can it be subsumed under utopian impracticality?

Consideration of ad hoc approaches to system design (as, indeed, *all* approaches *should*) start with a more or less explicit recognition of the fact that the designer does not have a magic wand.

A magic wand is a useful device. You can wave it and produce a hearty meal, a spendid castle, or a beautiful princess. Conceivably it could also be used to eliminate the *need* for food, shelter, or the opposite sex. Traditionally, however, the use of magic wands has been restricted to the task of modifying environments. System requirements are accepted as "givens"; the wand is used to provide environmental resources that will satisfy these requirements.

What happens when you don't have a magic wand?

Assuming you wish to continue to live (suicide is always a possible choice as contemporary existentialists continue to remind us), several alternatives present themselves.

In the first place, it is possible to *accept* your hungry, cold, or solitary state. In the jargon of some clinical psychologists and some Darwinian biologists, this is referred to as *adjustment*. Indeed, this may frequently be the only viable choice available. If it is difficult, you may obtain the services of a counselor; if it is impossible, you may pass away secure in the knowledge that you were not one of the "fittest" who were destined for survival.

As a second alternative, however, you might decide to *train* yourself to get along with minimum amounts of food, warmth, or love. Thus you could forage for scraps of food, use a cave for shelter, and accept the companionship of any harridan in the vicinity. In this alternative, as in the first, the environment is left relatively untouched. The discrepancy between system requirements (what your body thinks it needs) and environmental resources is made up by modifying the requirements.

As a third alternative, you might say, "I'm getting out of here," and depart for California or the South Sea Islands or New York or Alaska. This alternative, too, leaves the immediate environment untouched; it simply helps you choose a different environment as you might choose a different pair of socks. You have decided that you are in the wrong *place*.

Finally, you might say, "The problem is one of *time*. I can't have what I *really* want now. But if I clear the forest and plant crops and raise cattle and quarry rock and build a castle, some princess will find her way here and we can live happily ever after."

But life may not be quite as simple as this fourth alternative has led you to believe. Dragons may live in the forest. It may be necessary to slay the dragons before you can clear the forest. Before you can slay the dragon it may be necessary to forge a sword of steel. Before you can forge the sword of steel it may be necessary to discover how to make steel and why iron is important, and so on.

Each of these four alternatives, then, can be viewed as a substitute for low-level magic. The only significant difference between magic and any of them consists of the *amount* of time required to achieve results. In principle, *effort* is required in any case (even a magic wand has to be waved).

And it is precisely because they seem to neglect the time dimension that utopians are criticized most severely. To be preoccupied with plans that cannot be accomplished within a "reasonable span of time" is to be "divorced from reality" and, indeed, to be "utopian."

It seems to follow that if one *does* consider the time span for a specific project—if one is *practical*, if one considers present reality—then he has succeeded in discarding the more disconcerting qualities of utopianism.

But it is, unfortunately, quite possible to address oneself only to present reality and at the same time to be quite unrealistic, to be concerned only with practical ends while being completely impractical, to have an evolutionary *Weltanschauung* and preside over the termination of one's own species.

Let us examine some specific examples of ad hoc efforts and their associated utopian dreams.

The Utopia of Mercantilism

The term "mercantilism" seems to be a label for something similar to what we have been calling a "heuristic." In popular usage and indeed in the work of many serious historians and economists, it conveys the notion of an invariant principle of action used in the design of national economic systems during the seventeenth and eighteenth centuries. One formulation of this principle might read, "the most extreme state interference with economic life."[1] It represented an effort on the part of individual countries and their statesmen to increase national wealth for the specific purpose of increasing national military and diplomatic power or simply to help provide maximum degrees of national security.[2]

If you undertook to examine a specific economic system and noted the presence of activities definable as "government" or "external" interventions, you would be in possession of an inventory of mercantilist practices. If you were interested in designing a pet utopia, you could specify mercantilism as a guiding design principle. Within the framework of such a utopia, problems of unemployment or inflation, for example, might be dealt with through direct government intervention rather than left to the vagaries of a free-floating market structure.

But this view of mercantilism—the view that sees it as a heuristic or principle—is an inadequate view. Mercantilism is more appropriately understood as an ad hoc design technique. Let us see why.

Although the mercantilists represented the extreme of what today might be called state planners, the burden of their efforts often consisted of attempts to *remove* local controls of various kinds rather than to impose national controls. Thus, as Eli F. Heckscher has pointed out in his classic work on mercantilism, the so-called "toll system" which developed during the Middle Ages introduced trade barriers far in excess of those warranted by the purely technical difficulties existing in that period. In general, tolls were set up at points along internal water routes and in markets and towns, rather than at boundaries between political territories. Thus, by the middle of the sixteenth century, a merchant transporting goods along the Rhine River encountered a toll station every 15 kilometers.[3] And along the Rhone and

---

[1] Eli F. Heckscher, *Mercantilism* (London: George Allen & Unwin, 1935), II, 316.

[2] Cf. Overton H. Taylor, *A History of Economic Thought* (New York: McGraw-Hill Book Company, 1960), p. 82.

[3] Eli F. Heckscher, *op. cit.*, I, 45–57.

Seine Rivers, "toll charges formed the largest item in the cost of river transport."[4]

Additional trade barriers existed as a consequence of the utter confusion that arose from local jurisdiction over apprenticeship, gild membership, methods of manufacture, and the right to buy or sell. All of this illustrated "how utterly hopeless a system based upon local jurisdiction can become."[5] Businessmen who were constantly being harassed by local laws and regulations became eager allies to the state planners who were intent upon eliminating these restraints upon trade and manufacture.

But now it becomes clear that we can no longer insist upon viewing mercantilism as a heuristic that prescribes actions concerning government or other interventions. Under some environmental conditions mercantilism required such intervention; under other conditions it required an absence of intervention.

If we now proceed to consider mercantilism as an ad hoc approach to system design rather than as a heuristic, we must begin by understanding the contemporary reality with which it was confronted.

This reality included the existing domestic toll system; local privileges of various kinds; inequalities in the system of coinage, weights, and measures; and the absence of unity in legislation, administration, and coinage. As a result, many of the efforts of mercantilist planners were directed toward removing trade obstructions within a country and doing those things they saw as being necessary to keep economic life from being unduly limited to a restricted geographical area.[6] Thus, Colbert, the great French mercantilist and state planner par excellence, "never tired of reminding his intendants within the country and his governors in the colonies, or even threatening them with force, if they seemed to be placing obstacles in the way of trade."[7]

However, these threats never descended into a doctrinaire

---

[4] *Ibid.*, p. 80.

[5] E. A. J. Johnson, "The Age of Mercantilism," *Planned Society,* ed. Findlay Mackenzie (Englewood Cliffs, N.J.: Prentice-Hall, Inc., 1937), p. 83.

[6] Eli F. Heckscher, *op. cit.*, II, 273.

[7] *Ibid.*, p. 274.

insistence upon the necessity for freedom of trade as an invariant policy. The unstated though guiding philosophy of mercantilism seemed to consist of a notion that the structural characteristics of people should be accepted but that their environment must be reorganized in a way that would insure strengthening of the state. People, as operating units of these national systems, were not to be forced to do anything contrary to their own natural bents. The mercantilist design, in short, called for environmental manipulation to deal with the structural realities of human operating units.[8]

The ultimate aim of mercantilist planning was presumably to mobilize forces for national aggrandizement. To do this within the framework of contemporary reality, decisions were made to increase the population of the country, to train the common people in husbandry and the crafts, and to keep them accustomed to labor and, as far as this was possible, away from the consumption of luxuries such as sugar and tea. Decisions were made to produce the necessities of life at home as a precaution against foreign attack; to develop the merchant marine as an auxiliary to the navy; and to obtain large supplies of precious metals to help in domestic trade and to finance wars. In addition, decisions were made to direct private enterprise toward industries the government was trying to develop for national reasons, to insist that colonies obtain most of their manufactured goods from the home country and send raw materials in return, and so on.[9]

But in order to make these decisions it was necessary to begin by making some judgments about the existing state of the economic system, about the adequacy of one's analytic technology, and about the forces operating in the existing environment of that system. Thus, for example, it was necessary to understand what contemporary men within that system were like and what sorts of things would be most likely to motivate them. One did not begin by postulating an economic or any

---

[8] Cf. *ibid.*, p. 293.
[9] Wesley C. Mitchell, "The Social Sciences and National Planning," *Planned Society, op. cit.*, pp. 109–110.

other kind of man. One began by surveying the contemporary scene—in effect, codifying one's view of present reality and making decisions about specific activities that would lead to a "better" state of affairs.

To achieve the ultimate goal of mercantilism, it might at times be necessary to use government controls of various kinds and to invoke "freedom" of trade at others.

One of the elements in the mercantilist reality of English planners was the *fact* of sheep and woolen manufacture in England. Another was the fact that the population of England consumed the products of this sheep and woolen manufacture. Other facts included the need for grain to be used as food for domestic populations, and the possibilities for national profits under various price conditions. Against this background, it is interesting to observe the consequences of mercantilist planning and action. In the year 1571, Parliament passed a law that required compulsory wearing of woolen caps. In 1665, the dead were required to be dressed in woolen shrouds. In 1700, the English government forbade the wearing of Oriental silks and printed or painted calicoes. The English Corn Laws forbade grain exports. The wage clauses of the Statute of Apprentices gave Justices of the Peace control of the incomes of agricultural laborers. Export bounties were adopted to raise the price of grain when harvests were unusually large.[10]

If England had been a large silk-producing state—if that had been one of the confronting facts of contemporary mercantilist reality—presumably the heads of its citizens would have been adorned in silk; if aircraft and missiles had been invented, presumably the merchant marine would have suffered neglect; if automatic machinery had eliminated the necessity for unskilled or semiskilled labor, presumably no requirement would exist for either training common people in crafts or keeping them accustomed to labor.

In short, as we have previously indicated, specification of action within the framework of mercantilism demanded that the

---

[10] Cf. *ibid.*, pp. 96–97.

environment be assessed before anything else was attempted. Given the existing state of technological development during the era when mercantilism flourished, its "underlying thesis" becomes readily comprehensible. Manufactured goods were scarce, that is, they were not freely available, as was air or water in most locations. The national system seemed to need them. To make them available, it was necessary to have not only land and capital but also human labor. If every human being in society could somehow be converted into an operating unit and induced to work, more manufactured goods would become available. It thus became important to emphasize the virtues of work and the evils of idleness. One hundred per cent utilization of all human operating units became the operational definition of mercantilism's thesis. Efforts were made to make life more satisfying, or at least much less threatening for those who subscribed to and acted in a fashion consistent with that thesis.

The contrast with conditions existing, say, in the United States during the 1960's leads to a better understanding of some contemporary difficulties. Under a set of conditions in which "labor," in its traditional sense, has surrendered its primacy as a factor of production to automated and semiautomated production systems, or under conditions of market surpluses in many areas of the domestic economy, it is perhaps more easy to understand why idleness, for example, is no longer the bugaboo it was under conditions of the mercantilist environment. On the contrary, strictures against "moonlighting" by members of the labor force become a battle cry of organized labor, and efforts to reduce the length of the working week are strongly accelerated. Instead of proposals for compelling all members of society to engage in useful occupations or professions, studies of the use of leisure time and the feasibility of early retirement from working life are becoming increasingly more fashionable.

Within the framework of the mercantilist environment it was reasonable to argue that excessive consumption fostered discontent. From here it was but a step to the marshaling of public opinion and legislative action against "any attempt of the lower classes to ape the dietary or sartorial customs of the upper classes."[11] If the tastes of workingmen and their families were modest, it was possible to pay them modest wages. This, in turn, would help keep costs down and help provide a better competitive position on the international market. However, as early as the close of the seventeenth century, the possibilities inherent in expansion of the domestic economy had become apparent and "the hope of an improved standard of life was increasingly recognized as a powerful force which stimulates industry more certainly than low wages and Christian resignation."[12] But, of course, as long as the requirements for low production costs and a good competitive position on the international market were prime features of environmental reality, it was scarcely to be predicted that such changing insights could receive universal sanction.

One of the prime difficulties confronting mercantilist planners can thus be understood as an inadequate application of their own methodology. Policies which become rationalized as principles or heuristics are hampered by their own rationalizations. The weight of custom and special interest and the sheer momentum of social and economic practice place barriers in the way of a constant sensing of environmental realities and a reformulation of policies in terms of these new realities.

On the other hand, an orientation like that of mercantilism, which is geared exclusively to the realities of the present environment, is apt to be slow in promulgating measures designed to *change* that environment. It was much easier to enforce the wearing of woolen hats and shrouds than it was to develop a domestic silk or, let us say, a plastics industry. It was much easier to prolong the custom of low wages and low standards of living for laborers than it was to make the environmental adjustments that would provide incentives for increasing domestic standards of living. No one can reasonably accuse the mercantilists of having been impractical. But when seen against the framework of what it was possible for them to have achieved,

---

[11] E. A. J. Johnson, *op. cit.*, pp. 104–105.
[12] *Ibid.*, p. 105.

their efforts can be dismissed as another example of ineffectual and unrealistic utopianism.

THE UTOPIA OF LAISSEZ FAIRE

When mercantilism is viewed as a heuristic that connotes a great deal of government intervention, then laissez faire is its antonym. Defined as a *principle* of action, laissez faire would apparently connote the process of refraining from government intervention. If mercantilism involves centralized control of an economic system, then laissez faire implies decentralization and local freedom of economic action.

However, the paradoxical nature of this dichotomy is seen when we observe that the goal of mercantilist endeavor—great power for the state—was not translated into fact until the nineteenth century. And this mercantilist goal was achieved largely through the work of a laissez faire approach, although the efforts of this approach apparently were aimed in the opposite direction.[13]

In this connection, one version of the origin of the term laissez faire is especially interesting. In this account, the mercantilist Colbert asks a French manufacturer named Legendre to tell him what the French government could do for industry. The reply, "laissez faire" (let us alone), can be interpreted as the plea of a man who was relatively unconcerned with theoretical niceties—one who had assessed his own economic position, and had come to a conclusion about the kind of policy that would serve his own interests best. Had this same industrialist sold his industrial interests and emigrated to England to buy a farm, we might expect him to be one of the more ardent supporters of a high, government-imposed protective tariff on grain imports. His principle of action can scarcely be described as an invariant prescription of government nonintervention.

But what of the laissez faire theoreticians? Were they more rigid in their adherence to principle?

---

[13] Cf. Eli F. Heckscher, *op. cit.*, II, 326.

Adam Smith is the name that inevitably comes to mind in discussions of laissez faire theoreticians. He is, perhaps, the best known of them all.

Smith, it turns out, was somewhat partial to country gentlemen and farmers, albeit on theoretical grounds. Since these men are dispersed in different parts of the country, he tells us, they cannot combine as easily as can merchants and manufacturers who are assembled in towns. The latter, therefore, says Smith, were probably the original inventors of protective tariffs, which help give them a monopoly of the home market. Furthermore, it was probably in imitation of them that the country farmers and country gentlemen "so far forgot the generosity which is natural to their station as to demand the exclusive privilege of supplying their countrymen with corn and butcher's meat."[14]

But Smith was well aware of some of the environmental realities of his own time. He tells us that to expect complete restoration of free trade in England "is as absurd as to expect that an Oceana or Utopia should ever be established in it. Not only the prejudices of the public, but what is much more unconquerable, the private interests of many individuals oppose it."[15]

Among these private interests were members of parliament who, if they supported proposals for increasing monopolistic control of the home market, were "sure to acquire not only the reputation of understanding trade, but great popularity and influence with an order of men whose numbers and wealth render them of great importance."[16]

If, however, a member of parliament opposed such measures or succeeded in thwarting them, "neither the most acknowledged probity, nor the highest rank, nor the greatest public services can protect him from the most infamous abuse and detraction, from personal insults, nor sometimes from real danger, arising

---

[14] Adam Smith, *An Inquiry into the Nature and Causes of the Wealth of Nations,* Everyman's Library Edition (New York: E. P. Dutton & Co., Inc., 1910), I, 406.

[15] *Ibid.,* p. 414.

[16] *Ibid.,* p. 415.

from the insolent outrage of furious and disappointed monopolists."[17]

Another feature of this environmental reality that Smith found himself obliged to consider concerned the situation of a domestic manufacturer suddenly confronted with the competition of foreigners and obliged to give up his business. The problem of disposing of his plant and machinery would be considerable, and Smith warns us that changes of this sort should be introduced very slowly and preceded by a long warning period.

The distinguished successor to Adam Smith as a laissez faire system designer was David Ricardo. Ricardo wrote at a time when factory owners rather than country gentlemen and farmers had assumed leadership in economic affairs. The increasing efficiency of British manufacturing that accompanied the increasing progress of the Industrial Revolution made it advantageous to import food and raw material instead of producing it at home. Pressure was exerted upon farmers and landowners to lower rents and prices of farm goods. The country gentlemen and farmers quite naturally sought relief through government intervention that would protect their position. In short, the environmental realities existing in Ricardo's day had changed sufficiently from those existing in Adam Smith's day so that although they both professed adherence to the philosophy of laissez faire, the quality of Ricardo's laissez faire "aligned him generally *with* the business and *against* the agrarian community," in an almost complete reversal of Adam Smith's position.[18]

Thus laissez faire, as an approach to system design, involved a very special view of present reality. One might almost describe this view as one that saw the world as an encapsulating corsage of artichoke leaves surrounding an inner system heart. If one could but strip away the leaves, the system would emerge pure, if not succulent.

But somehow, one never quite reaches the heart. And one can readily become doomed to an eternity of endless leaf-strip-

---

[17] *Ibid.*
[18] Cf. Overton H. Taylor, *op. cit.*, p. 86.

ping. Historically, this seems to have been the fate of laissez faire designers.

Interestingly enough, among the *least* doctrinaire of these leaf-strippers were some of the early theoreticians of laissez faire. Adam Smith, for example:

> . . . did *not* assume that actual societies do or can or (at all probably) ever will fully realize his ideal regime, and he was more interested in understanding or explaining . . . actual patterns of behavior and events than in working out a full systematic theory of an unreal, ideal world. And he never . . . allowed his vision of what "ought to be" to obscure, distort or confuse his grasp of the current actualities which he sought to ascertain, describe and explain.[19]

The general problem to which Smith addressed himself was that of removing those governmental restrictions not conducive to the increase of wealth. He argued for the removal of national regulations that did a disservice to individuals and were disadvantageous to the community. However, he insisted that the government engage in many activities that were clearly beyond the interest of individuals or individual corporations.

Other theoreticians did engage heavily in conceptual leaf-stripping. Thus, David Ricardo, T. R. Malthus, Nassau Senior, John Stuart Mill, and others developed a comprehensive set of "laws" applying to a competitive market economy. The heart of their artichoke consisted of an "ideal" or "natural" state of individualism and free competition. Their "scientific" analysis was confined to an explication of how this heart would produce and consume goods—if only the leaves were stripped away.

But it was not only the theoreticians who engaged in leaf-stripping. Policy makers in countries such as Great Britain became very much involved in stripping away what happened to be the leaves of government intervention. One result of the Industrial Revolution was to give British industrialists a superior competitive position on the world market. Under these circumstances considerable pressure existed for the repeal of restrictions on the freedom of trade. In 1784, William Pitt's excise law was

---

[19] *Ibid.*, pp. 78–79.

repealed. This law had imposed a detailed system of regulation on the cotton industry. The law was opposed on the ground that it deprived manufacturers of "personal liberty and the free exercise of their property."[20]

In 1813 and 1814, several laws including the wage and apprenticeship clauses of the 1563 Statute of Artificers were repealed. These laws had regulated hours and had required justices of the peace to adjust wages in accordance with price fluctuations. After they had been repealed, public protection for workers was limited to poor relief for the unemployed and supplementary payments to those whose income remained below the subsistence level. Detailed regulation of the leather, baking, and Scottish linen industries was repealed between 1823 and 1827. In 1833, the commercial monopoly of the East India Company was abolished, and in 1834, restrictions on change of residence by the poor were lifted. The usury laws were repealed in 1854.[21]

But neither the theoreticians nor the policy makers ever quite succeeded in achieving the utopia they apparently sought. The perennial stripping of leaves never quite achieved the objective of uncovering an inner-system heart.

The heart would be a market economy—"an economic system controlled, regulated and directed by markets alone."[22] In this system, the orderly production and distribution of goods depends upon a self-regulating mechanism. It is based upon the assumption that human beings will behave in a manner designed to maximize their individual monetary gains. It also assumes the existence of markets in which the supply of goods and services available at a given price will equal the demand at that price. Such a system implies that all production is for sale in the marketplace and that all incomes are derived from such sales. Markets must exist not only for traditionally defined goods and services,

---

[20] Witt Bowden, Michael Karpovich, and Abbott Payson Usher, An Economic History of Europe Since 1750 (New York: American Book Company, 1937), p. 429.

[21] Cf. ibid., pp. 429–430.

[22] Karl Polanyi, The Great Transformation, 2nd ed. (Boston: Beacon Press, 1960), p. 68.

but for labor, land, and money as well. The prices for these are wages, rent, and interest, respectively.

But, as Polanyi has pointed out, ". . . labor, land and money are obviously *not* commodities; the postulate that anything that is bought and sold must have been produced for sale is emphatically untrue in regard to them . . . according to the empirical definition of a commodity, they are not commodities. Labor is only another name for a human activity which goes with life itself, which in turn is not produced for sale but for entirely different reasons, nor can that activity be detached from the rest of life, be stored or mobilized. . . ."[23] Similarly, neither land nor money is produced for sale. And Polanyi argues strongly that allowing the market mechanism to be the sole director of the fate of human beings, of their natural environment, or even of the amount and use of purchasing power would destroy society. Thus, during the nineteenth century, as markets developed throughout the world, they were increasingly accompanied by government policies designed to protect labor, land, and money from the unchecked influence of an unregulated market.[24] The leaf-strippers, in effect, were overcome by those environmental features that encouraged the growth of new leaves—leaves that perennially shielded the heart of their artichoke.

The twentieth century has witnessed an interesting use of the laissez faire technique in the arena of international politics. Here the currency of the unregulated marketplace is national power. All market participants seem to be more or less in agreement about the denominations of this currency. Bombs are measured in terms of equivalent TNT tonnage. Manned bombers are equated with intercontinental and other varieties of missiles. Armies are measured in terms of size, firepower, and degrees of combat readiness. Since the participants are nations rather than individuals or corporations, interference from "super-governments" or other forms of extranational control are resisted as interfering with the inalienable rights of individual national power. Individual human beings and their possessions are inexorably required to assume the status of power commodities.

---

23 *Ibid.,* p. 72.
24 *Ibid.,* pp. 73–76.

The heart of this twentieth century artichoke is an unregulated marketplace utopia of naked power. Armageddon becomes the mechanism for settling accounts.

EVOLUTIONARY DESIGN

Suppose you wished to construct a system that would continue to operate despite radical changes in its environment. Suppose you had no way of predicting what changes were going to occur in this environment. Suppose, finally, that you didn't really care about perpetuating your original system—that you would be satisfied as long as *some* system was always in operation no matter what the particular state of its environment happened to be.

You might do what many experienced, hardboiled administrators have been known to do on occasion: assign the system building task simultaneously and independently to many different designers, and wait.

Assuming you have selected your designers with a view toward insuring variability of results, you will soon find yourself with several different systems in operation. If environmental conditions change, presumably at least a couple of the systems will continue to exist. If you continue the process—that is, assign the task of building new systems to many different designers— you will, hopefully, have an operative system at any given point in time. You haven't predicted the environment, you haven't predicted future states of your system, you haven't considered the analytic technology necessary to proceed from one state of affairs to another. You have used an elementary form of a concept—"the survival of the fittest."

Charles Darwin is the one whose name is most often associated with this concept, although apparently he borrowed the term from Herbert Spencer and used it in preference to his own expression "natural selection."

Darwin illustrates the concept by describing the situation of a wolf that must survive by preying on various animals. He postulates a set of environmental changes that result either in a decreased supply of all prey except deer or a marked decrease in the number of deer during the season of year when wolves are hardest pressed for food. Under these circumstances the swiftest wolves would have the best chance of surviving. The wolf system that happened to maximize on speed would be the fittest and, consequently, the one to survive.[25]

One might easily modify Darwin's example and demonstrate a set of circumstances in which the swiftest wolves would be precisely the ones to disappear first. Suppose, for example, a colony of human sportsmen had established themselves in the vicinity for the purpose of going wolf hunting. Suppose these hunters found it convenient to keep the deer under observation, knowing that they acted as bait for the wolves. Now, the wolves closest on the heels of the deer—the swiftest ones—would be the first to appear in the sights of the hunters' rifles. The wolf system that had maximized on slowness might well be the one to discover other food sources and survive. The race for survival would go to the slow wolf.

Darwin's view of the "survival of the fittest" or "natural selection" was essentially an after-the-fact view. He examined part of the world about him and tried to explain how it got that way. Specifically, he was interested in explaining how living creatures got to their present states. His explanation is based upon two fundamental assumptions—the assumption of reproducibility and the assumption of variability. Living creatures reproduce themselves—but never without some changes occurring in the offspring.

Now these conditions can be achieved by a system designer who knows nothing whatever about the secret of life. If he has sufficient resources at his disposal, he can produce an endless number of systems and insure that some degree of variability is introduced into successive versions. As each of these versions vies for a favorable evaluation, we are confronted with a "struggle for existence." This concept is starkly simple in the Darwinian scheme of things. A creature system either lives or dies; problems of system evaluation become reduced to a single unmistakable

---

[25] Cf. Charles Darwin, *The Origin of Species* (New York: Modern Library, Inc., 1937).

criterion; and the story of evolution becomes a history of survivors rather than a tale of what might have been.

Underlying the entire evolutionary approach is an implicit assumption of helplessness in the face of environmental realities.

Consider for a moment the problem of a swift wolf who might decide to *survive* or to help other swift wolves survive under the conditions of our previous example—when the hunter colony arrived and the swift wolves became destined for extinction. To begin with, our swift wolf might provide himself with an environmental sensing capability, that is, an ability to examine the conditions under which an initial wolf was shot, or to obtain information about the arrival of hunters and details about their sport. It might then be possible to invoke a series of actions on behalf of swift wolves. Such actions might range from supplying the wolf population with bulletproof vests to convincing the hunters that target practice or baseball is a more satisfying form of recreation.

But the idea of getting wolves to convince wolf hunters to give up the sport is ludicrous. So is the notion of having wolves manufacture bulletproof vests for themselves. The former is ludicrous because we assume a high degree of stability in the environment. The latter is ludicrous because we assume a high degree of stability in the state of the wolf production system (for example, it produces freshly killed deer—not bulletproof vests).

But if we now step into the role of creator rather than creature, if we regard both the environment and system as open to redefinition, then neither of the two ideas is intrinsically unsound. We wave our magic wands and our hunters become baseball fans. We wave our magic wands again and our wolves become bulletproof vest manufacturers. On the one hand it is possible to make the mistake of believing that our magic wand can change only the *environment*. On the other hand, it is possible to assume erroneously that only the *system* can be changed —while the environment must remain constant for all practical purposes.

Historically, evolutionary designers have probably tended to err more in the second direction than in the first. Herbert Spencer went as far as to insist upon the "morality" of adaptation to an implicitly fixed environment. "All evil," he asserted, "results from the nonadaptation of constitution to conditions."[26] This includes all varieties of both "physical" and "moral" evil. "Every suffering incident to the human body, from a headache up to a fatal illness—from a burn or sprain to accidental loss of life is . . . traceable to the having placed that body in a situation for which its powers did not fit it. . . ."[27] However, Spencer reassures us, evil perpetually tends to disappear. The fact of nonadaptation to environmental conditions is continually being corrected. This is true for plants, animals, and human beings. Siberian herbs and shrubs, for example, adapt to a short arctic summer and speed through their life cycle in the space of a few weeks. Domesticated cows give more milk than wild cows. Man adjusts his diet to locally available foods and his tolerance to weather in accordance with local weather conditions.[28]

Samuel Butler's *Erewhon* describes a fictional society that defines morality in essentially these Spencerian terms. In *Erewhon*, illness is a crime. Moreover, "Ill luck of any kind, or even ill treatment at the hands of others is considered an offense against society . . . Loss of fortune . . . is punished hardly less severely than physical delinquency."[29]

In the words of an Erewhonian judge speaking to a boy who has just been convicted of having pulmonary consumption, "It is all very well for you to say that you came of unhealthy parents, and had a severe accident in your childhood which permanently undermined your constitution; excuses such as these are the ordinary refuge of the criminal; but they cannot for one moment be listened to by the ear of justice. I am not here to enter upon curious metaphysical questions as to the origin of this or that— questions to which there would be no end were their introduction

---

[26] Herbert Spencer, *Social Statics* (New York: Appleton-Century-Crofts, 1886), p. 73.

[27] *Ibid.*, pp. 73-74.

[28] Cf. *ibid.*, p. 74.

[29] Samuel Butler, *Erewhon* (New York: Modern Library, Inc., 1927), pp. 88–89.

once tolerated, and which would result in throwing the only guilt on the tissues of the primordial cell, or on the elementary gases. There is no question of how you came to be wicked, but only this—namely, are you wicked or not. . . ."[30]

Now if one could, by waving a magic wand, create an environment in which tubercle bacilli could not exist, the evil in the Erewhonian boy would presumably disappear. His guilt consists of being inappropriately adapted to his environment. Simple logic, however, tells us that the problem can be attacked from the perspective of *either* the boy or the environment. And this is precisely why the entire incident is humorous. Isn't it ridiculous, we say, to *blame* the boy for being sick? It's not *his* fault. It's the fault of those nasty old germs who thrive in his lungs. That judge would do better to see the boy to a hospital where someone could so alter the environment of those germs that they would leave him alone. Instead of doing the reasonable thing, the judge is insisting upon maintaining a fixed environment for both the boy and the germs. He then condemns the boy for "not belonging." Isn't that ridiculous?

But of course it is ridiculous only when seen from a special perspective. The argument of the judge could be placed, with virtually no revision, into the mouths of contemporary "realists" who have become wearied with post-Freudian clichés about unconscious motivation and arguments about social rather than individual guilt. The price of nonadaptation to society's legal environment is death or isolation. "Let us have no excuses or apologies please. You did not adapt; you must pay the price."

Even more sensitive souls concerned with efforts to "rehabilitate" the criminal frequently proceed from a premise of environmental fixity. Rehabilitation can readily be read as a synonym for adjustment.

However, rehabilitation ultimately refers to some kind of "good" behavior on the part of the person being rehabilitated. And one way to insure such good behavior is simply to insure that operating units are capable only of good behavior. In the last chapter, we considered some of the problems involved in the

---

[30] *Ibid.*, p. 107.

design of operating unit structures. Let us now see how this problem relates to operating unit survival in the context of evolutionary design.

Suppose, as a designer, you wished to build a system composed entirely of persons (or computerized machines) who could size up new environments and always act "good." How would you go about deciding what properties the brains of these persons or machines should have? What characteristics should be eliminated?

W. Ross Ashby has suggested that there is no absolute sense in which any natural or artificial brain is "good." He insists that every faculty of every brain is good only conditionally—that there exists at least one environment in which a brain will be *handicapped* because it possesses a given faculty.[31]

Thus memory is usually considered "good," but this is true only in an environment in which the past provides a clue to the future (Ashby says where the "future often *copies* the past; should the future often be the *inverse* of the past, memory is actually disadvantageous."[32] Ashby's point is somewhat inaccurately phrased. Memory can, of course, be useful under conditions in which the future does *not* frequently copy the past or when the future is an inverse of the past. If, however, the environment provides no *clues* to the future, it can indeed be dysfunctional. The point is illustrated by Ashby's example of a sewer rat facing the environmental conditions called "pre-baiting." Naïve rats are very suspicious and sample strange foods only in small quantities. If, however, wholesome food is placed at the same place for three successive days, a rat will on the fourth day eat poisoned food placed at the same location and die. A rat with no memory would be as suspicious on the fourth day as on the first and would live. Thus, prolonged contact with this environment leads, other things being equal, to the evolution of a diminished memory capacity in sewer rats.[33]

But this concept of evolution involves a closed system

---

[31] W. Ross Ashby, "Principles of the Self-Organizing System," *Principles of Self-Organization,* ed. Heinz Von Foerster and George W. Zopf, Jr. (New York: Pergamon Press, 1962), p. 264.

[32] *Ibid.,* p. 265.

[33] *Ibid.*

governed by a set of heuristics which specify the outcome—namely, sewer rats with diminished memory capacity.

A similar set of heuristics may, of course, be fed into a computer with similar consequences. Ashby's account of how zeros inherit a world is a case in point. A computer's memory is filled at random with digits from zero to nine. Life within the computer is arranged so that the digits are continuously multiplied in pairs with the right-hand digit of the product replacing the first digit taken. In this particular world, even times even produces another even. Odd times odd produces an odd. But, since even times odd produces an even, the evens have a better chance of survival. And among the evens themselves, the digits best suited for survival are the zeros, and it is, in fact, the zeros which ultimately inherit the world.[34]

Digits that permit themselves to be multiplied in this fashion are indeed helpless creatures. Their descendants are aptly called "zeros." One might with some justification assert that to be "good" in such a system is literally to be good for nothing. A "normal" (a "well-adjusted") digit is one that is neither more nor less than zero. But, of course, this is true only because of the special features of the environment in which these numbers are required to exist. A slight change in the rules of that environment (for example, adding nonzero, randomly selected constants to every new product) would completely change the basis for survival and make all zeros the legitimate object of rehabilitation efforts.

In short, Ashby's digits may be viewed as illustrative of evolutionary design in either a Hegelian or a Darwinian sense. Under the conditions described by Ashby, the design is essentially Hegelian in nature. The history of the class of digits described as zeros is foreordained. They will, sooner or later, inherit the earth. The fulfillment of their destiny requires only the passage of time and the occurrence of some finite number of calculations.

If, on the other hand, the rules of computation were periodically revised as we have suggested above, then all digits would be involved in a Darwinian struggle for adaptation to their changing environment and, indeed, for existence.

---

[34] *Ibid.,* pp. 271–272.

In both of these approaches, there is an implicit assumption that the environment lies beyond the control of the system within it. The rules of the environment are seen as being subject to the decision of a Dr. Ashby or some other creator.

But let us suppose for a moment that we are empirical observers of Dr. Ashby's digit system. We take a cross-sectional reading of this system at a given point of time. The usefulness of a Hegelian dialectic now becomes clear. To understand the meaning of the data we have collected, it is necessary to engage in a historical sort of analysis that tells us something about where these numbers came from, what they are *not*, and what they will eventually become. ". . . to express and define that-which-is on its own terms is to distort and falsify reality. Reality is other and more than that codified in the logic and language of facts."[35]

In Dr. Ashby's world, an odd digit may insist upon the fact that it is an odd digit. The passage of time and events will make it unmistakably clear that it is in point of fact an incipient even digit on its way toward becoming a zero.

Dr. Ashby knows this. He understands the destiny of his digits. But how does anyone else get to know it? How, for example, does a digit get to know its own destiny? And how does a digit design a system for accommodating to its environment in the face of the inexorable computer program that Dr. Ashby has decreed will define the fate of all digits?

One thing is clear. A methodology confined to the cross-sectional examination of facts at a point in time will be inadequate. Since we are now privy to Dr. Ashby's scheme for his universe, we can tell any of his system-designing digits that any fact obtained during a cross-sectional exploration will be, at best, a partial fact. To understand the system we must obtain data through time. We must, in point of fact, engage in what might be termed a historical or genetic investigation. We must understand what they *are* at present in terms of how they *arrived* at the present. We must understand that they are only transiently

35 Herbert Marcuse, "A Note on the Dialectic," Preface to *Reason and Revolution: Hegel and the Rise of Social Theory* (Boston: Beacon Press, 1960), p. x.

what they appear to be and in many senses not at all what they are. We can then hope to obtain some insights into the nature of the computer program that defines their destiny.

Sophisticated evolutionary design, then, involves the solution of several different kinds of problems. In the first place, it is necessary to provide a sensing device that can detect environmental changes. The environment may include such diverse features as the physical world, the climate of public opinion, the conditions of political reality, or the current state of technology. Since presumably any or all of these features may change through time, a design solution adequate for yesterday's features may be completely inadequate to deal with contemporary environmental conditions.

In addition to a sensing device, it is necessary to maintain a historical account of events as the system moves through time. This can provide some clues to the nature of the system's operating units and the presumptive character of their future states.

The system itself must be capable of finding alternate solutions to the problems it encounters, after assessing the state of its current environment and the capabilities of its currently available operating units. It must possess *program flexibility*, that is, it must have the capability and will to modify its accustomed patterns of behavior to deal with new configurations of environment and system state.

However, it is precisely this condition of program flexibility that becomes the most impractical and visionary feature of evolutionary design. Where programs of action are crystallized into equipment design, this rigidity becomes most apparent. To change the program requires a change in equipment—a new "model," which is both time consuming and costly. An alternative to equipment scrapping can often be found in the use of computer-instructed equipment where changes in the program of action can be made through changes in computer instructions or "computer programs." The impetus to make such changes must stem from the creators of the programs.

But, for better or worse, program creators tend to be prisoners of habitual thought patterns—what Thorstein Veblen called "institutions." As Veblen put it, ". . . Institutions are . . .

adapted to past circumstances, and are therefore never in full accord with the requirements of the present. In the nature of the case, this process of selective adaptation can never catch up with the progressively changing situation in which the community finds itself at any given time."[36]

Indeed, Veblen insists, the structure of a social system can change or adapt itself to a new situation "only through a change in the habits of thought of the several classes of the community; or in the last analysis through a change in the habits of thought of the individuals which make up the community. The evolution of society is substantially a process of mental adaptation on the part of individuals under the stress of circumstances which will no longer tolerate habits of thought formed under and conforming to a different set of circumstances in the past."[37]

To the extent that a part of the system is protected from environmental stresses, it will tend to retain outmoded and inefficient habit patterns. The folklore of industrial organizations is filled with illustrations of firms that have succumbed to competitive pressures because they grew "soft" in a protected noncompetitive environment. Veblen makes the same kind of point with respect to the "wealthy leisure class" which, he maintains, is in a protected position vis à vis economic forces.

Members of the leisure class are not required to change their habits of life or their theoretical orientation toward the external world as changes in industrial technique occur. They tend to be "conservative" and to oppose innovation, not because they necessarily have unworthy vested interests in maintaining the status quo, but rather because they are not "constrained" to urge changes by the pressure of their economic environment. Since this conservatism is characteristic of the wealthier and consequently the more respectable segments of society, it acquires an "honorific" value. "Conservatism, being an upper-class characteristic, is decorous; and conversely, innovation, being a lower-class phenomenon, is vulgar."[38]

---

[36] Thorstein Veblen, *The Theory of the Leisure Class* (New York: The New American Library, 1953), p. 133.

[37] *Ibid.*

[38] *Ibid.*, p. 138.

Veblen cautions us that conservatism is not necessarily bad. He is willing to entertain the notion, advanced by spokesmen of conservatism, that without some substantial resistance to innovation, social innovation might propel the community into untenable positions.

Again, the point to be made is a simple one: Habitual thought patterns can have the effect of insulating parts of a system from desirable environmental challenges. *Changing* these thought patterns can present serious problems to the evolutionary designer. Thus, for example, if your habitual thought pattern is focused upon yesterday's technical challenge (for example, "How can we build a bigger bomb and a faster delivery system?")— if you persist in viewing problems of system design through the filter of this technical challenge alone—it is perhaps inevitable that the system you design will be unresponsive to changing challenges of mission statements focusing upon the values of human integrity and survival. Of course, all this may be good or bad. One presumably should always be free to root for the values of either beauty or the beast.

EXISTENTIALIST DESIGN

Suppose we forget about systems for a moment— about computers, computer programs, display equipment, utopias, and all the rest. Suppose we take a very narrow view of the world—one seen exclusively through the eyes of a human being. We now contemplate the *human* situation rather than an operational or a scientific situation. We begin with a fact—the reality of human existence. We hold in abeyance any consideration of the characteristics or functions or the essence of man.

If we do this, someone will inevitably call us existentialists.

If you insist that man is just another of the objects cluttering up the earth's surface; that you could, if you were so disposed, simulate all of his senses and record all the environmental data he could possibly receive (perhaps more); that there is no good scientific reason for using his perspective in viewing the universe since more encompassing and even more interesting perspectives are available—we have no quarrel with you. We simply wish to begin with the fact of human existence because if we did not begin with this fact we would find it impossible to derive meaning from any of the other activities, including science, in which we might wish to engage. We do not accept the notions you provide about what man is. Perhaps he *can* be described—for your purposes—as one of a given class of objects. We cannot accept this description as sufficient for our purposes. Categories like time and space are simply insufficient for understanding the fact of existence.

This point of view seems to be completely at variance with a point of view implicit in the development of contemporary computer-based systems. Computers require schematic and abstract solutions to problems. These become known in the jargon of the trade as flow diagrams, computer programs, and so on.

But for the existentialist these schematic solutions would be seen as instruments of retrospection rather than as instruments of progress. Individual existence, they would insist, demands change, incompleteness, and lack of closure with respect to the future.

Now, starting with a concept like "existence" as our vantage point for viewing the world can be confusing. It can readily lead to the design of a system which, in technical terms, must be called "fantastic."

Jean-Paul Sartre once defined fantastic as "the revolt of the means against ends."[39] An object insists it is a means and then either conceals its end or refers back to another means. This in turn leads back to still another means, and so on. We can never discover the ultimate end. A bolted door is opened; it leads to a wall; you sit down and order coffee; the waiter repeats the order several times after having you repeat it several times; he notes the order in a book, gives it to a third waiter; a fourth waiter returns, places an inkwell on your table; you tell him you ordered

[39] Jean-Paul Sartre, "Aminadad or the Fantastic Considered as a Language," *Literary and Philosophical Essays* (New York: Collier Books, 1962), pp. 65–66.

coffee; he agrees; he walks off.[40] The heroes of fantastic stories never encounter anything useless; their worlds are completely populated by instruments, doors, staircases, waiters, and so forth. But, "These instruments are not . . . meant to serve them, but rather to manifest unremittingly an evasive, preposterous finality."[41]

In the "normal" world, a message presupposes a sender, a messenger, and a recipient. The message itself is a *means*. In a fantastic world, the message essentially assumes an isolated and independent existence. In such a world we are "plagued by messages without content, without messenger and without sender. Or the end may exist, but the means will gradually eat it away."[42]

What might actually happen in a fantastic world? Suppose we had designed and constructed an urban community with a well-thought-out transportation system including four-lane highways that circled the entire area. Highways, as everyone knows, are used to help motor vehicles move from one point in space to another. Motor vehicles on highways characteristically receive their energy from the combustion of gasoline. Suppose, now, that in our fantastic world gasoline assumed an independent existence and became an end in itself instead of a means. To be consumed in an internal combustion engine suddenly becomes suicidal incineration for the gasoline of our world. Gasoline tanks become residences. Large tanks are urban communities. Glass carburetors become high-status residences; the removal of non-combustible hydrocarbons serves to deprive our gasoline population of its accumulated savings. And so forth.

Or, again, assume that the transistors in electronic computers take on an independent existence and become ends instead of means.

What happens when *human beings* assume an independent existence?

Suppose it happened in a large Detroit automobile plant?

This seems to get a bit confusing. Presumably the assembly

[40] Cf. *ibid.*, p. 65.
[41] *Ibid.*, p. 67.
[42] *Ibid.*

line workers are on the assembly line precisely because they are conscious of their individual existence as human beings. They understand the need for clothing, food, and shelter for themselves and their families. That is *why* they appear on the assembly line.

But this is not completely accurate. The assembly line doesn't receive a complete human being. It receives a role—a foreman or a mechanic or a painter or an upholsterer. From the point of view of industrial management it is not only desirable, but absolutely essential, that the workers leave some of their human-ness behind when they enter the factory gate. Organized industrial effort, by its very nature, demands the subordination of individual human existence to the existential requirements of a task or final product. Under these circumstances, to insist that human beings working on an assembly line assume an independent existence is to insist that the industrial world become fantastic. Indeed, it is precisely this kind of juxtaposition that leads to so much misunderstanding between members of a work force and the management of a factory. If management assumes a relentlessly rational posture vis à vis the requirements of its task—that is, maximum production with minimum cost—and members of the work force assume a relentlessly rational posture vis à vis the requirements for individual existence, then the world of management is fantastic to the workers, and the world of workers is fantastic to management. Under these conditions, one can perhaps begin to understand why misunderstandings arise.

No industrial organization can survive in the face of complete and undisciplined freedom of action on the part of all its employees. The organizational structure and the industrial roles that it defines represent the "reality" to which individuals must adjust. Deviations for the purpose of providing existential freedom for an individual must be constrained. However, to the extent that human workers are replaced by automatons in industrial plants, this difficulty seems to be somewhat ameliorated. Our value structures characteristically do not include excessive concern for the freedom requirements of automatons or robots.[43]

---

[43] Cf. Robert Boguslaw and George R. Bach, "Work Culture Management in Industry," *Group Psychotherapy*, XII, No. 2 (June 1959).

The origin of the term "robot" is traceable to Karel Capek's play *R.U.R.* (Rossum's Universal Robots). In the fictional utopia described in this play, industrial effort is indeed completely delegated to automatons. The dramatic action turns on a revolt of the robots, who have developed an unplanned-for level of intelligence and intransigence and who ultimately exterminate their human creators.

Now it is quite possible to be a firm disbeliever with respect to whether this kind of play can or ever will be enacted off stage. A point that remains for consideration, however, is simply this: In what precise way are existing automatons inferior to human beings and why *won't* they revolt this afternoon?

The existentialist thinkers have some definite ideas on this subject. Jean-Paul Sartre, for example, might simply point out that contemporary robots are not *free* to revolt. It is this simple fact that distinguishes them from man. The destinies of these robots are recorded somewhere within their own heaven in letters of computer code. In this sense, robots have no future. They merely have a past that has not yet occurred. Sartre tells the story of a student who was confronted with a dilemma. He could either go to England and join the Free French Forces or remain with his mother whose need for him was desperate. The dilemma was complicated by the fact that everything he did for his mother was a "sure thing," that is, it would help her to carry on her own existence. On the other hand, efforts he might make to join the Free French Forces were contingent upon a whole list of possible eventualities. He might be detained indefinitely in Spain while en route to England; he might be stuck at a "desk job" after getting there, and so on. Thus, he really had two kinds of dilemma: (1) the practical problem of choosing between serving another individual (his mother), and serving a collectivity (his country); and (2) the problem of choosing between the ethics of personal devotion on the one hand and the ethics of devotion to a broader collectivity on the other.[44]

Now, if Sartre's student were an automaton, his dilemmas would be readily resolvable. Even if the designer of the autom-

---

[44] Jean-Paul Sartre, *Existentialism and Human Emotions* (New York: Philosophical Library, Inc., 1957), pp. 24–25.

aton had never envisaged the specific choice situation described above, he could have provided the machine with a decision principle (that is, heuristic) that would tend to make it decide questions of this kind on the basis of placing first in its value structure either loyalty to another person or duty to the collectivity. This might be adjusted to reflect the varying probabilities that no service at all could be rendered—and a decision could be cranked out in seconds. A nonexistentialist, for example, one who might see human beings as, let us say, completely the product of environmental conditioning and/or heredity, would insist that if we had all the relevant facts of the boy's background and experience, we could predict what his response would be. In this sense, it is possible to think of the human boy as an operating unit with more or less well-defined operating characteristics.

But the value structure of Sartre's student is different from either the computer or the nonexistentialist. The student decides to stay with his mother. It is the fact of remaining that defines his value structure. He is not only free to decide but indeed must decide. He cannot evade the choice. Men are free, Sartre tells us, and "things will be as man will have decided they are to be."[45]

All this needn't involve any mysticism. Some of our computer-programming friends would have great fun programming a computer to behave exactly as Sartre's student actually behaved. It is merely necessary to give the automaton instructions to make a random choice when confronted with a decision. It will then be possible to describe the character of the robot *post hoc* in terms of the actions it has actually taken. The existentialists would not be very taken with this solution, but it would seem, superficially at least, to incorporate all the operational features of Sartre's free man.

Our existentialist friends will point out that existing automatons won't revolt this afternoon because presumably they all have controls. They are not free. And, therefore, they are not human. They are not free to respond in an uncontrolled way to the realities of their environment. (In addition, of course, they

---

[45] *Ibid.*, p. 31.

are not very intelligent. They are somewhat like George Orwell's animals *before* the arrival of higher intelligence. Even if they were free they would not know how to deal with their environment very effectively. In this sense, however, they have many points of resemblance to all of us.)

But somehow all this does not really do justice to the existentialist view of the differences between human beings and automatons. In a word, human beings seem to be robots and *then-some*. The then-some is based upon a philosophical orientation that can be traced through Immanuel Kant, Henri Bergson, Søren Kierkegaard, Friedrich Nietzsche, Edmund Husserl, Martin Heidegger, Karl Jaspers, Martin Buber, and others. This is not the place to trace that orientation in detail, but perhaps it is possible to characterize the nature of then-some.

The quest for then-some occasionally seems to become a frantic search for an undefinable "thing" residing in the depths of man. Metaphysicians joyfully note that the "thing" has not as yet been discovered by scientists or information-processing specialists; scientists and information-processing specialists slyly hint to magazine editors that the thing will be found somewhere in the next batch of test tubes or in the next generation of higher-order computer languages.

For Henri Bergson,[46] this thing seems to consist of an ability to experience directly something called "duration" or "time." He gives to the ability the unfashionable label of "intuition," which is sufficient to make him unpopular with most people who like to keep close to respectable scientific tradition. For Friedrich Nietzsche,[47] the then-some is to be distinguished from simple reason or even intelligence. It is something we can call "emotion," "passion," or "will." For Martin Buber, the answer is to be sought not in an analysis of individual men, but rather in the distinctive quality of relationships existing between one human being and another.[48]

---

[46] Cf. Henri Bergson, *The Creative Mind* (New York: Philosophical Library, Inc., 1946).

[47] Cf. Friedrich Nietzsche, *The Philosophy of Nietzsche* (New York: Modern Library, Inc., 1954).

[48] Cf. Martin Buber, *Between Man and Man*, 5th ed. (Boston: Beacon Press, 1961).

But for our present purposes there is probably no need to inquire into some of the more basic philosophical issues inevitably raised by this discussion. Is there a *fundamental* difference between human beings and lower forms of animals or automatons? Let us remain agnostics on this subject. As empirical observers of human beings and contemporary automatons, it is indeed possible to report that they differ from each other both in perception and response. For at least the foreseeable future, human beings will continue to be plugged into even the most brave of our new systems. And, just as it is possible to make automatic equipment caricatures of human beings, it is possible to make human beings into caricatures of robots. Perhaps the fundamental danger in any system design is the possible loss of desirable aspects of "humanness." To avoid this danger, it is necessary to find means for insuring that the systems themselves somehow retain these qualities. If the design specifications are deliberately shorn of everything but a callous rationality, we feel uncomfortable without being able to specify why.

Some forms of ad hoc design can help provide a degree of assurance that recurrent opportunities will be available to compare current system states with current notions about what is important to us as human beings. This does not, of course, involve a descent into irrationality. For example, there are many good reasons for human beings to feel outraged at systems that rationally discuss the possible obliteration of humanity. Existence can scarcely exist without existence.

7

WHICH APPROACH IS BEST?

The conscientious reader who has followed us to this point will not really expect a direct answer to the question posed in the title of this chapter. To the extent that a direct answer is available, perhaps it will be found somewhere in the last chapter. But before proceeding, it is necessary for us to deal with some questions about the criteria we can use to determine the adequacy of any answer.

Which approach will minimize the amount of friction within a system or between one system and others? To what extent can simplified or standardized communication be used in a specific design approach to reduce operating difficulties and minimize friction or conflict? What approach will insure that operating units are continually kept well adjusted or trained to function most effectively? What approach minimizes organizational conflict?

FRICTIONLESS SYSTEMS

One of the by-products of *any* utopian renaissance ought to be a little peace and quiet. Ask any man on any street to de-

scribe utopia. He may see the government as monarchic, oligar-
chic, or democratic; the setting as rural, urban, or sylvan;
marriage customs as monogamous, polyandrous, or celibate—but
the *sound* in all cases will be envisioned as silence.

This is an interesting illusion because the more familiar
historical utopias have little soundproofing available. Sir Thomas
More's original Utopians abhor fighting and war but possess
many still-fashionable techniques for waging war effectively.
They propagandize enemies with promises of rewards for those
who kill their leaders. They attempt to generate internal difficulties within the enemy camp by aiding dissident elements. They
try to provoke external difficulties for the foe by stirring up
neighboring countries to fight for historic rights or privileges.

Campanella's *City of the Sun* is divided into seven huge
rings so built that anyone succeeding in storming the first ring
would find it twice as hard to take the second, and still harder
to take the third. Each succeeding ring is twice as difficult to
attack as the previous ring. Despite the reluctance of the inhabitants to accept money, they do barter with strangers but only at
the gates of the city. They sell the prisoners captured in war or
use them to dig ditches and perform other work outside the city
limits. Four bands of soldiers are used to guard the fields and
protect the prisoners who work them. They do not fight "except
on provocation" and have "artificial fires" for use in both land
and sea battles.

In Cabet's literary Icaria, the inhabitants "hope" for peace—
both internal and external. Nevertheless, all citizens are members
of a national militia and receive military training from the ages
of 18 through 20.

Examining our own contemporary societies under conditions
of "peace" we find innumerable examples of the absence of
"quiet." Stuart Chase, looking at his *New York Herald Tribune*
for May 4, 1950, a time of peace, found such items as:

U.S. Halts Sale of Armed Ships to Egypt
Republicans Hail Blow to Truman in Florida
Union Sues Oil Company
Ohio Court Bans Racial Bias at Pools

Rent Gouge Charged
Accuses Slain Man's Predecessor

If he were searching for analogous illustrations of quarrels and conflicts in the *New York Times* on May 4, 1964, he would find such items as:

Bulgarians Riot at Sofia Church
Brooklyn Boy Dies After Street Clash
300 at Klan Meeting Applaud Slurs on Negroes
Dominican Strike Imperils Regime—Police Clash with Crowds Supporting Walkout
Sukarno Orders "21 Million Volunteers" to March on Malaysia

Chase listed eighteen different areas of contemporary conflict. These ranged from personal quarrels, family feuds, community disputes, and sectional quarrels, to such things as worker-manager conflicts, political party disputes, as well as race, religious, ideological, occupational, industrial, national, and international disputes.[1]

Robin Williams, one of the more serious students of social institutions, noted some years ago that in *any* aggregate of human beings who have goals to achieve, the possibility of conflict arises. "Persons want scarce values, and their efforts to acquire them may not leave 'enough and as good' for others."[2]

This, of course, is highly reminiscent of the formulations of classical economic theorists in the eighteenth century tradition of Adam Smith and Ricardo; the nineteenth century tradition of John Stuart Mill; and the twentieth century tradition of Alfred Marshall and his descendants. The dismal science begins with a postulate of scarcity and builds an equilibrium analysis describing varying effects of supply and demand pressures on economic goods and prices under different sets of conditions. In this form of analysis the focus is characteristically placed upon "long-run" events. *Frictional* disturbances are seen as "short-run" dislocations, although the totality of economic competition is seen as a

---

[1] Stuart Chase, *Roads to Agreement* (New York: Harper & Row, Publishers, Inc., 1951), pp. 13–16.

[2] Robin Williams, *American Society, A Sociological Interpretation* (New York: Alfred A. Knopf, Inc., 1955), p. 203.

struggle among individuals who have disparate goals to achieve.

In the physical sciences, friction has a special meaning. It refers to the resistance encountered by one piece of matter as it contacts another piece of matter while moving from one place to another. An important ingredient of friction is the molecular attraction between two surfaces. Lubrication, which in the minds of laymen "smooths" things over, in fact is designed to reduce the mutual attraction between two bodies. Indeed, the "static friction" between two bodies increases as they are pressed together for extended periods of time.

Analogies are always dangerous. To mix one's physical and human analogies is especially hazardous; yet it is interesting to contemplate the consequences of a shift in vantage point. If one assumes the perspective of the designer of a physical system such as a gasoline motor, it becomes apparent that the reduction of friction at specifiable points is indispensable. It would scarcely do to permit pistons to develop enduring relationships with any portion of a cylinder wall. Lubrication helps the disaffiliation process. Since our value systems do not embrace a concern for the feelings of either the pistons or cylinders, we can only point to the fact that oil is "good" for both of them. It is not at all obvious, however, that oil is good for operating units when these happen to be human beings—that the designer should try to reduce friction in systems by facilitating a disaffiliation process.

ORGANIZATIONAL CONFLICT

The lack of congruency between the needs of individual human beings and the needs of organizations has become a truism of organizational theory. It is not only an individual's economic position that becomes involved, but his social status as well. Threats to wages, tenure, and control of one's own destiny endanger the only realistic life open to corporate employees.

Unions and other more informal organizations represent methods for dealing with these threats, but unionism is a means not only for alleviating a worker's economic insecurity, but for buttressing his sense of personal integrity as well.[3] It is, accordingly, not surprising to learn that, "Where compromise and conciliation end, industrial conflict begins; this conflict is an only somewhat muted version of war, and all the devices of war are familiar to the American industrial scene."[4]

Some years ago, I conducted a study of 70 management and union leaders of an industry in New York City who were engaged in collective bargaining with each other. Each of the 70 leaders was interviewed intensively and responded to a variety of research instruments including an attitude questionnaire and a sociometric test. A dominant recollection of the year I spent doing the study was one of having witnessed a great deal of peace but very little quiet.

The "staple" industry was engaged in producing a consumer product sold entirely in the metropolitan area. A large number of firms were engaged in collective bargaining relations with several unions representing their production and distribution employees.[5]

An initial difficulty in studying the collective bargaining game in this industry was the fact that there existed nothing remotely resembling a ball park. The bargaining sessions themselves were not available for observation and, in any event, a whole series of bargaining relationships appeared to be involved. There were many games going on simultaneously. Thus there were labor lawyers who represented several unions, management officials who had other business interests, union officials who were charged with having business interests in the staple industry itself, and the officials on both sides who apparently were motivated by political considerations of various sorts.

If "peace" is defined as the *absence* of strikes, lockouts, or similar examples of overt organizational strife, a great deal of peace seemed to exist in the "staple" industry during those days. If "quiet" is defined as the absence of *intra-union* or *intra-man-*

[3] Cf. *ibid.*, p. 191.

[4] *Ibid.*

[5] Cf. Lois MacDonald, Robert Boguslaw, and A. Matthew Lord, "Labor Relations Attitudes, A Study in a Segment of an Industry," *Proceedings, New York University Sixth Annual Conference on Labor*, 1953.

agement conflict, there seemed to be very little quiet in the staple industry in those days.

The absence of overt difficulties such as strikes or lockouts was all the more interesting because a superficial examination of conditions within at least some portions of the industry would have led to the prediction that the reverse should be true. Jobs were by and large routine, mechanization of manufacturing processes was rather advanced, working hours were inconvenient, and companies were large and relations relatively impersonal. My own conclusions about this discrepancy, partially verified by the results of the study itself and supported even more by the course of events years after the study had been completed, can be stated rather simply. Much of the existing employee discontent failed to rise to an overt level because of:

1. Discrepancies existing between the objectives of the union leaders and the interests of their constituents.
2. Discrepancies existing between the interests of employer industrial relations officials in these companies and the apparent interests of the management organizations which they represented.

The evidence, in short, indicates that in the staple industry the more obvious objectives of the union and management organizations involved did not represent a decisive influence in shaping the bargaining behavior of labor and management leaders. Leaders on the same side of the bargaining fence were not in unanimous agreement on the definition of success. On the contrary, intra-organizational rivalries frequently exerted a more compelling influence upon collective-bargaining behavior than did the more conventional disputes that occurred between management and labor. The behavior of the union and management leaders could best be predicted by understanding their individual roles and relationships, rather than by placing primary reliance upon the apparent motivations of their respective organizations.

I find it helpful to think of the union organizations and the management organizations as consisting of two similar triangles placed side by side as in Figure 1. The vertical barrier between the triangles represents a strike. In order for the condition of

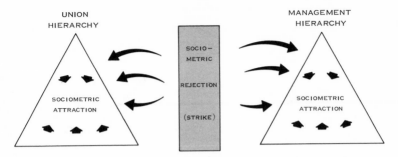

FIGURE 1. Struggle for Power Between Groups
(Quiet—No Peace).

strike to exist, it is necessary for both triangles to act with a high
degree of cohesiveness. There is of necessity a great deal of
internal solidarity which presumably could be measured through
appropriately designed sociometric tests and other measures.
One might well hypothesize that the greatest single source of
this solidarity is the presence of an opposing side and the very
fact of its opposition in a conflict situation. This is the state of
affairs popularly referred to as "closing ranks in the face of the
enemy." It will be observed that this was *not* the situation existing in the staple industry at the time of my study.

Now let us examine Figure 2. The situation in the staple
industry corresponded more to this diagrammatic representation.
No strikes or lockouts existed. The industry was formally at peace.
The solidarity that existed is indicated by the horizontal arrows
representing the measurable, close, sociometric relationships
between some top-level union leaders and top-level management
leaders. The lower horizontal arrows represent the sociometric
ties existing between lower-level union leaders and lower-level
management leaders. The hostilities that existed took the form
of internal struggles for power within both the union and management structures. These struggles left anything but a state of
quiet, although peace formally prevailed.

For the rank-and-file union member, it is clear that the
absence of strikes did not constitute a blessing on any level.

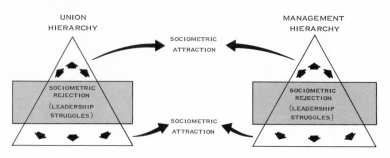

FIGURE 2. Struggle for Power Within Groups
(Peace—No Quiet).

Working conditions continued to be unsatisfactory; wages continued to be inadequate; heavy infighting left scars that were perhaps even more painful than those that might be received on the picket line.

For corporation stockholders, on the other hand, the situation was not, relatively speaking, much better. It is not at all clear that the decision to avoid strikes represented the best way to achieve maximum return on invested capital. In this industrial situation at least, the sublimation of conflict that occurred on an intra-organizational level involved costs that were demonstrably great and probably excessive to individual members of both the union and management organizations.

Figure 1 indicates what the probable situation would have been in the event a strike *had* been forced upon the leadership of both sides while other conditions remained relatively constant. Strong incentives to resolve temporarily the intra-union and intra-management difficulties would have been provided by the fact of industrial warfare. Presumably the lines of sociometric attraction would reflect this increased strength of internal solidarity.

But there is little reason to believe that a strike would result in an enduring solution. The situation would presumably revert to our Figure 2 situation, and internal power struggles would again become the order of the day.

To be both blunt and simple, the major realistic differences existing in this industry consisted of economic struggles for a larger share of the industry's profits. In this sense, management and union members were all very much in the same boat. The more successful persons in each camp were those who did not permit themselves to be bound by the constraints of organizational identification and sought allies wherever they were to be found. The strongest allies were characteristically to be found among the leaders of the opposing organization.

Conflict Reduction

The tradition of Elton Mayo and the "human relations" approach to problems of industrial conflict is one that has evoked many provocative controversies bearing directly on these issues. A careful consideration of these controversies has been made by Henry A. Landesberger in his *Hawthorne Revisited.*[6] Perhaps the most fundamental criticism of the Mayo school is a charge that it neglected to consider the

> problem of conflict and conflicting interests of the parties in industrial relations and has therefore failed to look for the causes as well as the implications of this conflict. As a consequence, the energy, attention and enthusiasm of the group have been directed toward concepts and phenomena which are, by comparison, superficial and even trivial: status strivings of employees, relationships in informal groups in the factory, the need for catharsis through a counselor, and improving "communications," for example.[7]

Landesberger, in his defense of Mayo, points out that "the absence of organized labor-management conflict at Hawthorne does not imply . . . that a state of conflict did not exist. It implies only that this conflict did not exist in the form which has become the most notable since then, that is between organized labor and management."[8]

The conflict existing at Hawthorne was comparable to that diagrammed in our Figure 1, with two exceptions:

1. The hierarchies involved were not union and management

---

[6] Henry A. Landesberger, *Hawthorne Revisited* (Ithaca, N.Y.: Cornell University Press, 1958), pp. 28–47.

[7] *Ibid.*, p. 30.

[8] *Ibid.*, p. 64.

but informally organized groups of workers on the one hand
and groups of supervisors and technologists on the other.
2. The battle consisted of informal skirmishes on the issue of
production figures rather than of the formal warfare of a
strike.

Mayo has been accused of having both a pro-management
and a clinical bias shown in the apparent surprise he and his
associates experienced at discovering that workers have feelings
which contradict the cost-and-efficiency logic of management.[9]
This discovery leads to the observation that management people
lack the communications or human relations skills necessary for
effective supervision. This observation, in turn, leads to such
remedies as the training of supervisors in human relations. But,
as William Foote Whyte and others have pointed out, the only
available systematic research studies of such programs are far
from encouraging although participants in general seem to enjoy
the programs and say they get a good deal out of them.[10]

Another well-advertised approach to conflict reduction in
organizations relates to the apparently straightforward matter
of written communication. To a casual observer, it would seem
that helping employees in an organization to eliminate "gobbledygook" would be a move in the direction of increased efficiency—
that by reducing communication difficulties, organizational fric-
tions and conflict would be reduced. But is this always or even
usually the case?

One might ask the questions: Does gobbledygook really consist of nothing but indiscriminate ambiguity? Does it have any
utilitarian functions in an organization, whether the organization
be a government agency or a business firm? If so, what are they?
What characteristics of a bureaucracy compel the use of a gobbledygook device? How well does gobbledygook do its job?

Congressman Maury Maverick, who coined the term several
decades ago, once explained its origin. It came to him in a vision,
said Maury. "Perhaps I was thinking of the old turkey gobbler

---

[9] Richard Bendix and Lloyd H. Fisher, "The Perspectives of Elton
Mayo," *Review of Economics and Statistics,* XXXI (1949), 312–319.
[10] William Foote Whyte, *Man and Organization* (Homewood, Ill.:
Richard D. Irwin, Inc., 1959), p. 5.

back in Texas who was always gobbledygobbling and strutting with ridiculous pomposity. At the end of his 'gobble' there was a sort of 'gook.' "[11]

On March 30, 1944, Maverick, then chairman of the Smaller War Plants Corporation, issued an order to employees of that agency prohibiting the use of "gobbledygook" language. As defined by Maverick, "gobbledygook" consisted of "talk or writing which is long, pompous, vague, involved, usually with Latinized words. It is also talk or writing which is merely long, even though the words are fairly simple, with repetition over and over again, all of which could have been said in a few words."[12]

Maverick was not, of course, the first or only critic of this type of language. H. L. Mencken once summarized the situation by saying: "Public job holders, talking one with another, . . . are predominantly pretentious and shabby, and they are greatly given to counter words and clichés. This is true equally of the British and American species."[13]

The apparently obvious antidote for gobbledygook is exact communication through the use of symbols or codes whose meaning is completely unambiguous. Again, the availability of computer technology seems to provide the means for simply doing away with the curse of gobbledygook in organizational communication.

But let us take a somewhat closer look at gobbledygook and see what happens when it is eliminated in a specific communication:

Example 1

Gobbledygook Passage

Proper application of prescribed preventive maintenance measures must be a prime consideration in order to minimize replacements. Vehicle equipment of tactical organizations and that of administrative units and reserve pools should be interchangeable wherever possible in order that needed replacements for forward

---

[11] Maury Maverick, "The Case Against Gobbledygook," *New York Times Magazine* (May 21, 1944), p. 11.

[12] *Ibid.*

[13] H. L. Mencken, *The American Language*, Supp. I (New York: Alfred A. Knopf, Inc., 1945), p. 412.

areas be secured by inter-organization transfers to meet emergencies in which normal channels of supply would introduce delays.[14]

Alternate Method of Expression

Replacements must be kept at a low level by a rigid system of truck servicing. When emergencies cut off the normal flow of supply, all trucks in the unit, plus those in reserve pools, should be pressed into service by making transfers within the organization.[15]

This specimen of gobbledygook, described as a "monstrosity," has been extracted from a U.S. Army official handbook published in 1943. The alternate method has been suggested by a correspondent of H. L. Mencken.

We note immediately, of course, that the alternate method is shorter (45 words as opposed to 60 for the original). How was this reduction achieved? The table shows the specific substitutions that have been made and indicates some of the results of these substitutions.

An examination of the table shows that in Example 1 gobbledygook represents, in the first place, little more than a routine form of expression that possessed a somewhat stilted quality since more popular alternate methods of expression were available. In addition, however, gobbledygook performed the function of communicating more completely the message of the bureaucrat. "Simplification" was achieved at the expense of important omissions and distortions of meaning.

Example 2

Gobbledygook Passage

While freely conceding that the Soviet regime exhibits certain features which the humanitarian may be inclined to deplore, we must, I think, agree that a certain curtailment of the right to political opposition is an unavoidable concomitant of transitional periods, and that the rigors which the Russian people have been called upon to undergo have been amply justified in the sphere of concrete achievement.[16]

---

[14] *Ibid.,* p. 16.

[15] *Ibid.*

[16] George Orwell, "Politics and the English Language," *A Collection of Essays* (New York: Doubleday & Company, 1954), p. 173.

Gobbledygook Passage	Alternate Method of Expression	Numerical Difference in Words	Result
1. "Proper application of prescribed preventive maintenance measures"	1. "a rigid system of truck servicing"	−1	1. Substitution of slightly inaccurate popular terminology for a formalized method of bureaucratic expression.
2. "must be a prime consideration in order to minimize replacements."	2. "replacements must be kept at a low level by"	−1	2. Simplification of expression with no significant omissions or change of meaning.
3. "Vehicle equipment of tactical organizations and that of administrative units and reserve pools"	3. "all trucks in the unit, plus those in reserve pools"	−3	3. This appears to be an example of a logical "fallacy of division" committed by Mencken's correspondent. Because "trucks" are included as part of the general expression "vehicle equipment," it is assumed that "vehicle equipment" includes nothing but "trucks." Note especially that this omits any reference to spare parts, which is, apparently, the major consideration, since the passage begins by referring to the importance of "preventive maintenance measures."

Gobbledygook Passage	Alternate Method of Expression	Numerical Difference in Words	Result
4. "should be interchangeable wherever possible in order that needed replacements for forward areas be secured"	4. "should be pressed into service"	−10	4. The notion of "interchangeability" has been omitted here. "Pressed into service" does not seem to convey the necessary information.
5. "by inter-organization transfers"	5. "by making transfers within the organization"	+3	5. This apparent error becomes understandable as a direct result of the correspondent's previous inaccuracy in substituting the word "unit" for the expression "of tactical organizations and that of administrative units."
6. "to meet emergencies in which normal channels of supply would introduce delays"	6. "when emergencies cut off the normal flow of supply"	−3	6. Substitution of slightly inaccurate popular terminology for formalized bureaucratic expression.

Alternate Method of Expression

"I believe in killing off your opponents when you can get good results by doing so."[17]

Although this passage is "artificial" gobbledygook, in that it was composed by George Orwell for illustrative purposes, we may examine it here as a legitimate example. Orwell concludes that contemporary political expression to a considerable extent represents the "defense of the indefensible." He points to the purges occurring in the U.S.S.R. under Stalin and the American action of dropping an atomic bomb on Hiroshima as things that can be defended—but only by arguments too barbaric for most people to face and inconsistent with the platforms of all political parties. Defending the indefensible pushes politicians into the use of language that is euphemistic, question-begging, cloudy, and vague.[18]

Without attempting to evaluate the validity of Orwell's somewhat sweeping generalization, we may note in this example that the net effect of the gobbledygooking has been to soften the impact of the expression "killing off your opponents" by using a euphemistic device. Thus the utilitarian function of gobbledygook in Example 2 consists of translating a brutally frank statement into terminology that can arouse little resentment.

Example 3

Gobbledygook Passage

Upon consideration of a plan for joint action filed with the Office of Defense Transportation by the persons named in Appendix I hereof to facilitate compliance with the requirements and purposes of General Order ODT 3 Revised, as amended (7 F.R. 5445, 6689, 7694; 8 F. R. 4660, 14582; 9 F. R. 2793, 3264, 3357, 6778), a copy of which plan is attached hereto as Appendix II, and

It appearing that the proposed coordination of operations is necessary in order to assure maximum utilization of the facilities, services, and equipment, and to conserve and providently utilize vital equipment, materials, and supplies of the carriers, and to provide for the prompt and continuous movement of necessary traffic, the attainment of which purposes is essential to the successful prosecution of the war;

---

[17] *Ibid.*
[18] *Ibid.*

It is hereby ordered, that:
    The plan for joint action above referred to is hereby approved and the carriers are directed to put the plan in operation forthwith, subject to the following provisions, which shall supersede any provisions of such plan that are in conflict therewith. . . .[19]

Alternate Method of Expression
Fast Freight Lines, Inc.
    and
Trustworthy Trucking Company
Gentlemen:
    You recently filed with us a plan for joint action. We approve it and you can start right away. Follow these rules: . . .[20]

Rudolph Flesch discusses the implicit shortcomings of his own suggested alternate method of expression by observing that the Federal Register is not a simple medium of communication. "All this government stuff, in other words, is not reading matter, but prefabricated parts of quarrels."[21] These quarrels range from questions about the authority of an agency to do what it is doing to deliberate misunderstandings about grammatical constructions. The gobbledygook specifies the authority in minute detail, and uses cumbersome but unmistakable and defensible grammatical constructions. Plain talk will be achieved only at the expense of future controversy.

Thus, Example 3 illustrates the use of gobbledygook as a "prefabricated part of quarrels." Setting forth rigid descriptive specifications in meticulous detail is one way of meeting the need for legal exactness in government communications. Legal exactness is a means for making the ground rules of conflict available to all participants and to any interested observers who wander onto the scene.

Gobbledygook is *not* simply semantic folderol. It is a mechanism for dealing with deeply rooted ambiguity and a cosmetic that can be applied to the surface of deeply rooted conflict situations in organizational life.

It seems clear, in short, that the Utopia of industrial welfare

---

[19] Rudolph Flesch, *The Art of Plain Talk*, 2nd ed. (New York: Harper & Row, Publishers, Inc., 1946), p. 164.
    [20] *Ibid.*, p. 165.
    [21] *Ibid.*

is not to be achieved through a semantic cleanup any more than it can be achieved through simply increasing the social sensitivity skills of its inhabitants.

But how about education? Aren't most difficulties, in the last analysis, attributable to individual or collective ignorance? Won't the collecting and dissemination of more and better data make not only industry but the world in general a better place in which to live?

Before jumping to any such conclusions, one should carefully read a penetrating article by Wilbert E. Moore and Melvin Tumin entitled "Some Social Functions of Ignorance."[22] The central thesis of this paper is stated in the following terms:

> . . . ignorance is both inescapable and an intrinsic element in social organization generally, although there are marked differences in the specific forms, degrees, and functions of ignorance in known social organizations.[23]

Examples of the functions of ignorance cover a wide range. Thus, eliminating ignorance can have such consequences as destroying the basis for privileged or differential positions. Ignorance on the part of consumers of medical or legal services for example helps preserve the privileged positions of physicians and lawyers. One defense against this possibility is the generation of specialized languages and tools that can be used only by possessors of the appropriate information. Ignorance protects the expert from potential competitors. The most common device used to guard against this danger is the control by the experts themselves of training and thus of access to privileged positions.[24]

Eliminating ignorance can have the effect of destroying fair competition in a market system. If each participant knew all the policies, strategies, and decisions of his competitors, the very basis of competition would be destroyed. In bureaucratic organizations, ignorance acts not only as a means for avoiding jealousy over unequal salaries, but as a way of creating incentives by

---

[22] Wilbert E. Moore and Melvin M. Tumin, "Some Social Functions of Ignorance," *American Sociological Review*, XIV, No. 6 (December 1949), 787–795.
[23] *Ibid.*, 788.
[24] *Ibid.*, 789.

introducing uncertainty, anxiety, and risk into the economic
lives of organization men.[25]

SQUARE SYSTEMS VS. SWINGING SYSTEMS

Square—Conformist, Organization Man, solid citizen, anyone who
doesn't swing and isn't with it . . . Man, if you still don't dig
me you'll never be anything but. . . .[26]

The use of ignorance, gobbledygook and simple lack of
effective communication as policy instruments is well understood
by successful organization men. These men are not at all "square."
On the contrary, they tend to be quite "hip," and "swing" with
uninhibited abandon. They are rapidly learning to utilize the
new gobbledygook of computerese and "science" to achieve their
own ends in a world filled with impressionable laymen.

The authentic squares of our times are to be found among
social scientists who insist upon a preoccupation with after-the-
fact facts of life; intellectuals who concern themselves with
rationalizations about society rather than with the realities of
social issues; engineers and "hard" scientists who blithely deal
with system data presented to them for analysis without wishing
to ask questions about the broader context that lends more
complete meaning to these data; and the beatniks who withdraw
completely from all meaningful involvement in the affairs of their
times from motives of indolence, ineptitude, or fear.

The world, in a very real sense, belongs to those who know
how to harness the dominant ethos of their times while escaping
personal entrapment by that ethos. In mid-twentieth-century
Western Civilization this ethos clearly includes a deep-seated
reverence for organizational forms and perhaps an even deeper
respect for the wonders that surround blinking lights and pushbuttoned consoles.

The historic pronouncement that what is good for General
Motors is good for the country becomes an organizational rally-
ing cry broad enough to include such improbable allies as IBM,

---

[25] Cf. *ibid.*, 792–794.
[26] Lawrence Lipton, *The Holy Barbarians* (New York: Grove Press,
1959), p. 318.

the John Birch Society, or the City of Santa Monica. It is the kind of pronouncement that helps promote the reification of organizational forms; it is a pronouncement promulgated for the edification of squares.

The technology of blinking lights and pushbuttoned consoles decrees that the best system is one that minimizes internal organizational conflict, eliminates gobbledygook, and makes communication more efficient through increasing reliability and minimizing error. It seems clear that these constitute criteria for square systems only. They are humorless and, indeed, naïve criteria to establish for system effectiveness in the modern world. They are based upon a more or less deliberate exclusion of the most significant system variables from the design process. What are these variables? They are those that swingers insist upon withholding from the squares. A swinging system is one that serves the purposes of the swingers. To understand how these purposes come to be achieved, it becomes necessary to examine the use of power in systems and the systematic means through which power is achieved. We now turn to this final task.

8

THE POWER OF SYSTEMS AND SYSTEMS OF POWER

One of the more popular pastimes developed in the wake of a rapidly burgeoning high-speed computer technology has been the game of "let's play you think computers are bad and I think they are good." In one reported encounter, the protagonists were Norbert Wiener (the father of cybernetics) and Arthur L. Samuel (one of IBM's bright sons). Wiener stated as his thesis that "machines can and do transcend some of the limitations of their designers, and that in doing so they may be both effective and dangerous."[1] Samuel, invoking the familiar argument that "most, if not all, of man's inventions are instrumentalities which may be employed by both saints and sinners,"[2] concluded that "the modern digital computer is a modality whose value is overwhelmingly on the side of the good."[3]

History does not record a score for this particular contest, but one is tempted to question whether the game was played in

---

[1] Norbert Wiener, "Some Moral and Technical Consequences of Automation," *Automation Implications for the Future,* ed. Morris Philipson (New York: Random House, 1962), p. 163.

[2] Arthur L. Samuel, "Some Moral and Technical Consequences of Automation—A Refutation," *ibid.,* p. 179.

[3] *Ibid.*

the right ballpark. The Wiener thesis seems to proceed from a perspective that sees the computer as something like a bow and arrow contraption possessing more or less indeterminate, boomeranglike performance characteristics. Samuel seems to see his product essentially as a better mousetrap (and who wants to be on the side of the rats)?

There is, of course, at least one additional perspective from which we may contemplate the computer. This is the perspective that helps us to see it as an integral part of a larger, more encompassing social structure. Computers are not found in nature. They have to be built. And they must take their places within a framework of existing social systems. A decision to place them within a framework redefines existing system arrangements in significant ways. Indeed, as computer complexes assume functions previously performed by bureaucratic hierarchies or disparate units or unorganized work groups, they almost invariably lead to the redesign of existing systems. Specifically, this means changes in information organization (with the aid of computers or other physical equipment), formalized work procedures (that is, customs, computer programs, organizational directives, and so forth), and people.

The process of engaging in this redesign inevitably raises issues about how various system "functions" are to be accomplished. Without becoming embroiled in the intricacies of several hoary controversies among anthropologists and sociologists about the precise meaning of function and the usefulness of "functional analysis," we may note a formulation that defines function as the contribution an activity within a system makes to the whole.[4] This definition points up the importance of "specifying precisely both the part and the whole to which a functional statement refers. A practice which is functional within one social region need not be functional in one which is more (or less) inclusive."[5]

The credo of an engineer designing systems composed exclusively of physical or "hardware" components includes the

---

[4] Harold Fallding, "Functional Analysis in Sociology," *American Sociological Review*, XXVIII, No. 1 (February 1963).
[5] *Ibid.*, 6.

assumption that all functions performed by the components will be *manifest* (that is, "intended and recognized" by the designer).[6] *Latent* functions (those that are neither intended nor recognized) are hopefully omitted. The same credo is held by designers of classical utopias.

The difficulties that arise when computerized systems are designed *without* deviating from this credo have become legend among sophisticates. Suppose, for example, you wish to "automate" the communication functions carried on within a large system. A preliminary step must consist of a detailed specification of the various classes of information currently being communicated. To obtain such a specification, one might examine messages transmitted in the past, and perhaps codify the information normally transmitted over telephone or telegraph lines, and so on. In the process of conducting such an examination, it is all too easy for the neophyte to overlook classes of information characteristically transmitted, let us say, during coffee breaks. Ignoring the latent communicative function of the coffee break can result in a highly complex computerized system that has no way of dealing with some of its most crucial categories of system information.

As Robert K. Merton expressed it many years ago, "any attempt to eliminate an existing social structure without providing adequate alternative structures for fulfilling the functions previously fulfilled by the abolished organization is doomed to failure."[7]

Now one of the most pervasive characteristics of all social structures is the fact of social differentiation. This, in itself, does not seem very startling. We are accustomed to the notion that some people are old and some young, some female, some male, and so forth. Social differentiation becomes a matter for controversy only after it is used as a basis for social stratification: the distribution of unequal rewards among the various participants in a social system.

---

[6] Robert K. Merton, "Manifest and Latent Functions," *Social Theory and Social Structure,* rev. ed. (New York: Free Press of Glencoe, Inc., 1957), p. 51.

[7] *Ibid.,* p. 81.

Many years ago, two sociologists (Kingsley Davis and Wilbert E. Moore) tried to explain these differences essentially on the basis that "*if* the more important, highly skilled, and physically and psychologically demanding positions in a complex division of labor are to be adequately filled both from the standpoint of numbers and of minimally efficient performance, *then* there must be *some* unequal rewards favoring these positions over others."[8]

It seems clear that the particular scale of unequal rewards existing in a society tends to be self-perpetuating. People become accustomed to the allocation of certain differences in reward and tend to resist drastic changes.[9] A president of an industrial firm makes more money than a charwoman—this is considered appropriate and fair; and anyone who suggested a reversal in the reward system for our society would encounter serious resistance, not only from presidents, but from most "reasonable" people— including charwomen.

In designing a computerized system on the site of a previously existing "manual" social structure, one inevitably must deal with the effects the new system will have on previously existing roles and their incumbents. When the role incumbents are unskilled or semiskilled workers whose more or less routinized jobs are assumed by the computerized installation, this takes the form of concern with "technological displacement" and consideration of the consequences of "automation." The dialogue may proceed along lines of "these displaced workers must be trained for new skills—like computer programming; however, some people are untrainable and they constitute the core of the social problem accompanying automation. This is something like what happened when the automobile replaced the horse and buggy—new jobs will emerge for which people can be trained— the blacksmiths will simply have to face reality, and so forth."

In terms of social stratification, the human, low-skilled

---

[8] Cf. Dennis H. Wrong, "The Functional Theory of Stratification: Some Neglected Considerations," *American Sociological Review*, XXIV, No. 6 (December 1959), 774.

[9] *Ibid.*

workers are simply eliminated. They are not just placed at the bottom of the status and economic-reward ladder; they are removed from it.

But this removal inevitably has direct consequences for those who remain. The middle-level bureaucrat whose value consisted primarily of the uncodified information in his desk, file, or head now finds that he has been asked to furnish all relevant information to a central repository. Much of the prior basis of his unequal reward has been removed. The second- or third-level executive whose value consisted of an ability to analyze large quantities of data and come up with significant policy recommendations now finds his data analysis can be done more effectively according to predetermined analytical schemes. The highly skilled and psychologically demanding positions become those relating to operations of the computer and the formulation of computer programs.

All this, of course, shakes the foundations of existing stratification realities. Former "key decision makers" begin to feel, and indeed are regarded, as anachronistic hangers-on. Experienced computer experts have many techniques for dealing with this problem. One approach is to point out that the locus of decision making still rests with the former executive or manager. This, of course, is not really true. Disbelievers see the light when they ask for a given set of figures or ask that a pet procedure be implemented.

The answer, all too frequently, becomes "but the program can't handle it." Or, "We can't do that just yet, but in about six months, after these immediate problems are ironed out, I'm sure we can get that for you." Or, "This set of figures will cover about 98 per cent of all the cases you could possibly be interested in; it just wouldn't be economical to try to get 100 per cent of all the cases," and so on.

To an executive accustomed to getting his own way from human employees, even if they have to work overtime or develop ulcers in the process, this may all sound like an unpardonable affront to managerial prerogatives. He is thus inexorably driven to the next step in the process—the "I want a computer course" step. The feeling seems to be: "If I could only learn a little about computer programming, I could keep those snotty kids from being in a position to tell me how to run my business."

But, unfortunately, computer courses for executives seldom provide enduring solutions. At best, the executive learns to deal with his frustrations by accepting the frame of reference of the computer expert and adjusting his sights accordingly. The exercise of power, which formerly was mediated through conventions of law, custom, "what the union will stand still for," or "principles of human relations"—now must be mediated through the current state of computer technology.

To proceed in this fashion (that is, through technology-screened power) is to adopt an orientation that is essentially formalist in nature (although the work of Newell, Simon, and Shaw in the area of heuristic programming provides the promise of creative alternatives). The specification of future and current system states within this orientation characteristically requires an insistence upon a uniformity of perspective, a standardization of language, and a consensus of values that is characteristic of highly authoritarian social structures. Nonconforming perspectives, language, and values can be and, indeed, must be excluded as system elements.

All this is a familiar pattern in classical utopias. Although the inhabitants of utopian societies were frequently prepared to deal with external threats, internal dissension was almost invariably taboo. The tradition of specifying functions within computer-based systems enhances the points of structural correspondence of these systems and classical utopias. In this connection, Ralf Dahrendorf's summary of the structural features of utopian societies provides some useful insights. He points out that: 1) Utopias do not grow out of familiar reality or follow realistic patterns of development. 2) Utopias characteristically have universal consensus on values and institutional arrangements; that is, they are highly uniform throughout. 3) Utopias are characterized by an absence of internal conflict; that is, they are characterized by social harmony, which helps to account for their stability. 4) All processes within utopian societies follow recurrent patterns and occur as part of the design of the whole.

5) Utopias are characteristically isolated in time and space from other parts of the world.[10]

The simple fact of the matter seems to be that classically designed computer-based systems, like classical utopias, resolve problems of conflict, consensus, and reality by simple fiat. But these old problems do not thereby simply fade away. Environments change. Internal conditions change. Systems and utopias alike must be ready and able to change if they are to survive. But crucial types of change originate *within* systems—out of the contradictions and conflicts existing between two or more opposing sets of values, ideologies, roles, institutions, or groups.[11]

To insist that social structures must always be shaped and controlled from "topside," is to reinforce maladaptive tendencies in systems and to help to insure their ultimate collapse. A façade of value homogeneity cannot resolve the internal stresses, conflicts, and dilemmas that arise in any system designed to cope effectively with the fact of change.

Power and Bureaucracy

The problem of understanding what it is that makes human societies "stick together" or cohere has been studied by philosophers and social theorists for thousands of years. In general, two different kinds of explanation are offered. The first of these emphasizes the role of *consensus*—the existence of a general agreement on values within the society. The second explanation emphasizes the role of *coercion*—the use of force and constraint to hold a society together.[12]

One of the interesting limitations of traditional utopias is the relative lack of detailed concern they reflect about the composition of the glue used to hold things together.

---

[10] Cf. Ralf Dahrendorf, "Out of Utopia: Toward a Reorientation of Sociological Analysis," *The American Journal of Sociology*, LXIV, No. 2 (September 1958), 116–117.

[11] Cf. Pierre L. Van Den Berghe, "Dialectic and Functionalism: Toward a Theoretical Synthesis," *American Sociological Review*, XXVIII, No. 5 (October 1963), 699.

[12] Ralf Dahrendorf, *Class and Class Conflict in Industrial Society* (Stanford, Calif.: Stanford University Press, 1959), pp. 157–159.

In the *consensus* formula for social glue, people with common values voluntarily associate to help insure more effective cooperation. In the *coercion* formula, positions within the system are defined to insure effective application of force and constraints.[13] To understand the operation of any system, it is crucial to understand the distribution of authority and power within it. Differences in system design may, in the last analysis, involve little more than different allocations of power and authority throughout the system. Indeed, alternate arguments about the merits of different system design formats may well involve little beyond implicit rationalizations for alternate modes of power distribution.

Each of these formulas is based upon a set of assumptions about the nature of society or social systems. The consensus formula assumes that society is a relatively stable and well-integrated structure of elements, each of which has a well-defined function. Throughout the system itself, there exists a consensus of values among its various members. The coercion formula assumes that every society is at every point subject to both processes of change and social conflict. It further assumes that every element in a society contributes to the system's disintegration and change. And finally, the coercion formula assumes that every society is based on the coercion of some of its members by others.[14]

It is clear, of course, that these sets of assumptions are not necessarily mutually exclusive. As Dahrendorf has expressed it,

> There can be no conflict, unless this conflict occurs within a context of meaning, that is, some kind of coherent "system." No conflict is conceivable between French housewives and Chilean chess players, because these groups are not united by, or perhaps, "integrated into," a common frame of reference. Analogously, the notion of integration makes little sense unless it presupposes the existence of different elements that are integrated.[15]

The point to be stressed here, however, is the importance of specifying the exact nature of the particular glue to be used in a

---

[13] Cf. *ibid.*, p. 169.
[14] Cf. *ibid.*, pp. 161–162.
[15] *Ibid.*, p. 164.

specific system design. Perhaps the easiest error to make is the one that assumes that a consensus glue exists, when in point of fact the design either requires, or has surreptitiously imposed, a coercion formula.

To clarify this somewhat, it may be helpful to note how power, in the sociological sense, is differentiated from force on the one hand and authority on the other.

Force, in this context, refers to the reduction, limitation, closure, or total elimination of alternatives to the social action of one person or group by another person or group. For example, "Your money or your life," symbolizes a situation in which the alternatives have been reduced to two. Hanging a convicted criminal exemplifies the total elimination of alternatives. Dismissal or demotion of personnel in an organization illustrates the closure of alternatives. An army may successively place limitations upon the social action of its enemy until only two alternatives remain—to surrender or die.[16]

Power refers to the ability to apply force, rather than to its actual application. It is the "predisposition or prior capacity which makes the application of force possible."[17]

Authority refers to institutionalized power. In an idealized organization, power and authority become equivalent to each other. The right to use force is attached to certain statuses within the organization. "It is . . . authority in virtue of which persons in an association exercise command or control over other persons in the same association."[18] Examples of the use of authority include: the bishop who transfers a priest from his parish, the commanding officer who assigns a subordinate to a post of duty, a baseball team manager who changes a pitcher in the middle of an inning, and a factory superintendent who requires that an employee complete a task by a given time.[19]

"Your money or your life," constitutes what in the computer trade would be called a binary choice. If the alternatives available were extended to include, let us say, "the twenty-dollar bill

---

[16] Cf. Robert Bierstedt, "An Analysis of Social Power," *American Sociological Review,* XV, No. 6 (December 1950), 733.

[17] *Ibid.*

[18] *Ibid.,* 734.

[19] *Ibid.*

you now have in your pocket," "room and board at your home for two days," "a serviceable overcoat," "the three bottles of scotch you have in your closet," or "a friendly chat over a good meal," then the intensity of the force being applied might be seen as somewhat diminished. This is simply another way of noting that the exercise of force is related to the range of action alternatives made available. The person with the ability to specify the alternatives—in this case, the person with the gun—is the one who possesses power.

And so it is that a designer of systems, who has the de facto prerogative to specify the range of phenomena that his system will distinguish, clearly is in possession of enormous degrees of power (depending, of course, upon the nature of the system being designed). It is by no means necessary that this power be formalized through the allocation of specific authority to wield nightsticks or guns.

The strength of high-speed computers lies precisely in their capacity to process binary choice data rapidly. But to process these data, the world of reality must at some point in time be reduced to binary form. This occurs initially through operational specifications handed to a computer programmer. These specifications serve as the basis for more detailed reductions to binary choices. The range of possibilities is ultimately set by the circuitry of the computer, which places finite limits on alternatives for data storage and processing. The structure of the language used to communicate with the computer places additional restrictions on the range of alternatives. The programmer himself, through the specific sets of data he uses in his solution to a programming problem and the specific techniques he uses for his solution, places a final set of restrictions on action alternatives available within a computer-based system.

It is in this sense that computer programmers, the designers of computer equipment, and the developers of computer languages possess power. To the extent that decisions made by each of these participants in the design process serve to reduce, limit, or totally eliminate action alternatives, they are applying force and wielding power in the precise sociological meaning of these terms.

Indeed, a computer-based system in many ways represents the extreme of what Max Weber called a *monocratic bureaucracy*. For Weber, bureaucracy was "the most crucial phenomenon of the modern Western state."[20] He regarded it as completely indispensable for the requirements of contemporary mass administration. It possesses the advantages of precision, speed, unambiguity, knowledge of the files, continuity, discretion, unity, strict subordination, and reduction of friction, material, and personal costs.[21] Above all, it provides the "optimum possibility for carrying through the principle of specializing administrative functions according to purely objective considerations. . . . The 'objective' discharge of business primarily means a discharge of business according to *calculable rules*. . . ."[22]

The power position of a bureaucracy, Weber tells us, is normally overpowering. "The absolute monarch is powerless opposite the superior knowledge of the bureaucratic expert. . . ."[23] For example, the decrees of Frederick the Great concerning the abolition of serfdom were derailed by the bureaucratic apparatus, which regarded them as the occasional ideas of a dilettante. And Russian czars were seldom able to make permanent changes that displeased their bureaucracy or hurt the power interests of the bureaucrats.[24]

One of the most powerful tools available to a bureaucracy is secrecy. To the extent that members of a bureaucracy can keep their knowledge and intentions secret, they increase the importance of "professional know-how."[25]

Perhaps the most significant implication of bureaucratic organization is the tendency to convert all political problems into administrative problems. Karl Mannheim explained this phenomenon by noting that the activity sphere of an official is bounded by the limits of laws already formulated. The genesis or

---

[20] Max Weber, "The Essentials of Bureaucratic Organization," *Reader in Bureaucracy,* ed. Robert K. Merton, Ailsa P. Gray, Barbara Hockey, and Hannan C. Selvin (New York: Free Press of Glencoe, Inc., 1952), p. 24.

[21] H. H. Gerth and C. Wright Mills, eds., *From Max Weber: Essays in Sociology* (New York: Oxford University Press, Inc., 1958), p. 214.

[22] *Ibid.,* p. 215.

[23] *Ibid.,* p. 234.

[24] *Ibid.*

[25] Cf. *ibid.,* p. 233.

development of new law lies beyond his scope. "As a result of his socially limited horizon, the functionary fails to see that behind every law that has been made there lie the socially fashioned interests and *Weltanschauungen* of a specific social group. . . . He does not understand that every rationalized order is only one of many forms in which socially conflicting irrational forces are reconciled."[26]

Mannheim's conception of "politics" and "political problems" was not, of course, confined to government situations. "Politics" in his definition includes all situations in which decisions cannot be made in accordance with clear precedent or according to the clear requirements of an existing rule. Under these conditions, a bureaucracy characteristically finds means for taking action or making "political" decisions by manipulating the rule structure within which it operates. In the Congress of the United States, this device is the basis for the enormous power held by chairmen of congressional committees. Thus, the House Rules Committee has the apparently innocuous task of clarifying the procedures under which a given bill will be debated by the House of Representatives. Perhaps because here the bureaucrats (members of the committee and especially its chairman) are also politicians par excellence, this simple bureaucratic administrative device has for years been converted into one of the most potent political forces in the capital. In the world of industry, a traditional technique invoked by employees who do not wish to take the final overt step of strike action consists of rigid adherence to *all* operating rules within an organization. By invoking their essentially bureaucratic prerogative to observe either the "spirit" or the "letter" of organizational rules, employees can make the difference between a profitable operation and one doomed to failure. Indeed, there are serious system dysfunctions accompanying bureaucracies operating in virtually every kind of organization. To operate successfully, a bureaucracy must reach a high degree of reliability of response and conformity to prescribed rules. Under these conditions, the rules tend to be treated as absolutes rather than as relative to a given set of purposes. This, in turn,

---

[26] Karl Mannheim, *Ideology and Utopia* (New York: Harcourt, Brace & World, Inc., 1936), p. 105.

leads to difficulties in adaptation to new conditions that have not been anticipated clearly by those who drew up the rules. It thus seems to be an almost universal characteristic of bureaucratic structures that they result not only in dislocations in the patterns of power, but that in addition, "the very elements which conduce toward efficiency in general produce inefficiency in specific instances."[27]

One of the more violent teapot tempests generated in connection with contemporary discussions of high-speed computers is the controversy swirling about questions like, "Are computers intelligent?" and "Can computers think?" Paul Armer, of the RAND Corporation, has summarized and presumably disposed of some of the "negative arguments" on the subject. *The Argument by Invidious Comparison* is similar to a complaint that the first airplanes were not "flying" because they could not travel coast to coast nonstop, or because they could not land in a tree like a bird. *The Argument by Superexcellence* complains that computer musical compositions compare unfavorably with musical masterpieces. Armer slyly points out that many men cannot compose musical masterpieces. *The Argument of Definition* complains that behavior is not intelligent unless carried out by a living organism. *The Argument by Stipulation* insists that the notion be dismissed out of hand by simply asserting that what machines do is *not* to be called "thinking." *The Argument by False Attribution* simply misunderstands machine behavior, for example, it insists that chess-playing machines operate only by examining all possibilities. *The Argument by False Extrapolation* is based upon the assumption that computer characteristics are invariant to a given state of the art. This ignores such changes in technology as the development of transistors during a vacuum tube era. *The Obedient Slave Argument* fails to see intelligence in machines since they presumably can do only what they are instructed to do. Armer points out that there are no well-defined limits upon what it is possible to tell a machine to do.[28]

---

[27] Robert K. Merton, "Bureaucratic Structure and Personality," *Social Theory and Social Structure, op. cit.*, p. 200.

[28] Paul Armer, "Attitudes Toward Intelligent Machines," *Datamation* (March 1963), pp. 36–37.

In many ways, Paul Armer is refurbishing a hoary controversy that used to bedevil Sunday supplement editors. This is the controversy about the "real" nature of "human" nature. As Norman R. F. Maier (and others) pointed out years ago, the term "human nature" is characteristically used as a screen to hide our ignorance about man in general. And one of the more elementary oversights made in discussions of human behavior consists of ignoring the fact that the actions of men are set in motion by external as well as internal forces.[29]

But the totality of external forces that help shape human behavior includes much more than such obvious environmental factors as temperature, light, and atmospheric pressure. It includes the effects of other individuals and groups that exert different kinds and magnitudes of force at different times and in different situations. Even the most "intelligent" of intelligent human beings is not immune from the influence of forces external to him—forces that can shape, mold, or condition his organizationally relevant behavior. Armer's point is fundamentally quite simple. He is saying, in effect, "I challenge you to describe any role within an organizational context currently or traditionally occupied by a human being. I will take that description and, knowing the requirements of the role, will devise a computer program or a piece of computerized equipment that will not merely replicate appropriate behavior, but indeed will do it more efficiently than most human beings you might place in the role. If the performance of my program or equipment does not reflect 'intelligence,' then neither you nor I know what intelligence is. Come to think of it, if you let me have any standard intelligence test, bet I could program a machine to get a genius score on it."

And he could.

All this is vaguely reminiscent of the old musical comedy song in which the female human being insists to a male human being that, "Anything you can do, I can do better." Armer's computer somehow recalls the spirit of Annie Oakley. A helpless human being is completely on the defensive as he tries to assert

---

[29] Cf. Norman R. F. Maier, *Psychology in Industry*, 2nd ed. (Boston: Houghton Mifflin Company, 1955), pp. 8–9.

the distinctive character of his human-ness to a machine that can compose better symphonies, write better poetry, play better chess, and be a better manager than Mr. Average Joe Human. He knows he's different from the machine—but can he prove that he's any *better?*

Probably not.

As a matter of fact, if we insist that a bureaucratic structure is expected to reach a high degree of reliability and conformity to prescribed rules, it can probably be easily demonstrated that a computerized bureaucracy can meet these criteria more readily than a humanized one. And if one insists upon providing an operational definition for intelligence, it is clearly within the scope of existing or prospective computer technology to replicate or surpass human intelligence as defined in these terms. A fully computerized bureaucracy possesses all the advantages that Max Weber claimed for his ideal type. ". . . the more the bureaucracy is 'dehumanized,' the more completely it succeeds in eliminating, from official business, love, hatred, and all purely personal, irrational, and emotional elements which escape calculation. This is the specific nature of bureaucracy and it is appraised as its special virtue."[30]

But, of course, even the purest ideal type of bureaucracy does not behave in this fashion. The crux of the matter lies in the area of problem definition. "Trivial" exceptions to general rules can be handled either by implicit delegation to individual bureaucrats or through a more central source that generates the rules in the first place.

The place at which definitions are made of the precise meaning of the rules within which the bureaucracy must function is the point of maximum bureaucratic and political power. The simple fact of the matter is that whether your bureaucracy is composed entirely of the most intelligent human beings imaginable, or of the most intelligent machines available, it is the definition of the rule structure that becomes the central fact of significance in defining the structure of power relationships. For example, given a specific problem such as racial discrimination

---

[30] H. H. Gerth and C. Wright Mills, eds., *op. cit.*, p. 216.

in a northern industrial center, and a set of facts, how does the problem get defined? Suppose the set of relevant facts consists of the following statements: 1) A large portion of the Negro workers have a low industrial output traceable to low morale stemming from continued discrimination. 2) A large number of white workers object to any proposal designed to eliminate segregation.

Robert K. Merton has described two contrasting definitions of the problem that can "reasonably" arise in this situation. One definition asks, "How can we make segregation tolerable or palatable to the Negro worker?" Under this definition the bureaucratic (or machine) task becomes one of finding effective propaganda to be directed toward the Negro population. The purpose of this propaganda would be to increase morale without removing segregation. A second definition of the problem may be addressed to finding ways to remove segregation without significantly lowering the morale of white workers.[31]

Let us now make a further assumption, namely, that the cost of pursuing one course of action is exactly equal to the cost of pursuing the second. To a cost-minded executive the specific course of action adopted may well be a matter of indifference— the bureaucratic rule may well be stated in terms that provide complete degrees of freedom to the bureaucrat or the computer programmer as long as the fundamental criterion of cost is appropriately observed. It is obvious, however, that the precise policy finally adopted could have extensive consequences not measured in terms of immediate organizational cost. The bureaucrat or machine possessing the power to make this trivial decision is indeed powerful in a nontrivial sense.

VALUE DILEMMAS AND COMPUTERIZED SYSTEMS

Replying to arguments about the possible superiority of computers over human beings can be an upsetting experience— if one happens to identify with the perspective of people. Sociologists, anthropologists, and other students of human behavior

[31] Cf. Robert K. Merton, "Role of the Intellectual in Public Bureaucracy," *Social Theory and Social Structure, op. cit.*, p. 217.

are familiar with this experience. In countless other contexts they have seen it as an indication of ethnocentrism—the view that one's own life or tribe or customs are to be preferred over all others. Anthropologists have long been familiar with the curious phenomenon that in the language of many nonliterate people the name of the tribe frequently means "human beings." Implicitly, everyone to whom the tribal name does not apply is outside the pale of humanity. And, for example, "When the Suriname Bush-Negro is shown a flashlight, admires it, and then quotes the proverb, 'White man's magic isn't black man's magic,' he is merely reaffirming his faith in his own culture. He is pointing out that the stranger, for all his mechanical devices, would be lost in the Guiana Jungle without the aid of his Bush-Negro friends, at ease among its dangers."[32]

So, it comes as a very small surprise indeed to those who believe that the crucial ingredient of the human condition is high-order intelligence that an argument such as Paul Armer's (purporting to demonstrate that computers are potentially just as smart as the rest of us) must be rejected out of hand. We all tend to be somewhat ethnocentric about the tribe of humanity. We *know* we have magic that Armer's cottonpickin' machine couldn't possibly have.

What precisely is it that we have in addition to that mechanistic kind of IQ which Armer implies is our last remaining talent?

As a minimum, we have a sense of values. Some things are important to us. Other things are not so important. As sophisticates of twentieth-century civilization rather than members of a nonliterate tribe, we can accept the possibility that Paul Armer's computer might not only be able to replicate our values, but might even dream up a set demonstrably better for us than our own. But they wouldn't be ours. And they wouldn't be the machine's. They would be Paul's. And that's the rub.

On the face of it this seems almost insulting to Paul Armer and his colleagues in the information-processing profession. These men do not have any readily discernible political axes to grind.

---

[32] Cf. Melville J. Herskovits, *Man and His Works* (New York: Alfred A. Knopf, Inc., 1948), p. 68.

They are neither politicians, labor leaders, nor representatives of big business. They are scientists and engineers—objective experts whose only concern is technical efficiency and scientific detachment. It seems grossly unfair to imply that they act with devious motivations and for the promotion of hidden causes.

The point, of course, is simply that values are not derived either scientifically, logically, or intellectually. They are simply prime factors. And even if Armer's values were those of a saint, we might well wish to promote our own saint with a somewhat different set of values to be implemented. But, says the information processor, "I do only what the customer tells me to do. I implement the values of someone else, rather than my own. And in the absence of specific instructions, I use as a guide line the criterion of technical efficiency or cost, or speed or something similar."

All this is true, and it brings us once again to the inescapable fact that power in the design of large-scale computer-based systems resides to an increasing degree with 1) the customer—to the extent that he can specify in complete and rigorous detail exactly what decisions he wishes to see implemented by his bureaucracy under every conceivable set of conditions, or, 2) the system designer and computer programmer, who insure that *some* decision is made in every case whether that case has been clearly anticipated or not, and 3) the hardware manufacturer, whose technology and components determine what kind of data can be sensed and processed by computers, display equipment, and other system equipment.

To the extent that customers (and these may include government agencies or private industry) abdicate their power prerogatives because of ignorance of the details of system operation, de facto system decisions are made by equipment manufacturers or information-processing specialists. The customers may find it impossible to specify all future situations; they may be unable to devise foolproof heuristics; they may fail to specify detailed operating unit characteristics; they may be unable to devise appropriate ad hoc plans. Under each of these conditions, de facto decisions are again made for them by system designers or other technical specialists.

As computer-based systems become increasingly more significant in shaping the realistic terms of existence in contemporary society, it becomes increasingly more relevant to inquire about the implications contained for expression of individual values. The process of obtaining representation for individual values is one of the specific notions contained in popular conceptions of democracy. However, the central idea of democracy has been penetratingly described as "one particular way in which the authority to govern is acquired and held."[33] Thus, "A man may be said to hold authority democratically when he has been freely chosen to hold such authority by those who must live under it, when they have had, and will have, the alternative of choosing somebody else, and when he is accountable to them for the way in which he exercises this authority."[34]

It is, of course, clear that there are limits on the democratic principle and that legal and institutional safeguards must exist to protect values other than those of democracy itself. It is equally clear that at best the democratic principle can be only approximated. No one in our society seriously suggests that every person must be absolutely equal to every other person in power and influence.[35] But, "the working touchstone of a 'democratic' system of authority is simply the degree to which it gives individuals legitimate instruments for reaching those who make the decisions that affect them, and for bringing influence to bear upon them. A system is more or less 'democratic' depending on the number, availability, and effectiveness of these instruments, and on the proportion of the population entitled and able to use them."[36]

Now, whether the "masses" are denied legitimate access to decision makers by reason of despotism, bureaucratic deviousness, or simple technical obfuscation, the resultant erosion of democratic process can be much the same. To the extent that decisions made by equipment manufacturers, computer programmers, or

---

[33] Charles Frankel, "Bureaucracy & Democracy in the New Europe," *Daedalus* (Proceedings of the American Academy of Arts and Sciences), XCIII, No. 1 (Winter 1964), 476.

[34] *Ibid.*

[35] Cf. *ibid.*, 476–477.

[36] *Ibid.*, 477.

system designers are enshrouded in the mystery of "technical" detail, the persons most affected by these decisions (including customers, publics, and employees) will be denied the opportunity to participate or react to the decision made. The spectrum of values represented in the new decision-making order can and is being increasingly more circumscribed by fiat disguised as technological necessity. The paramount issues to be raised in connection with the design of our new computerized utopias are not technological—they are issues of values and the power through which these values become translated into action.

A major difficulty is the lack of clarity involved in efforts to specify values in exact terms. Frequently, values are expressed in terms of principles or heuristics. Thus, some of us value property rights, others value political, social, or more generally, "human" rights. Partisans of the extreme political right as well as those of the left and many in between insist upon their espousal of values which, when stated as heuristics, all sound the same. Yet it is clear that the value orientations of "conservative" political groups are fundamentally different from the value orientations of "liberal" political groups. It is clear that such differences include at least the following:

1. Differences in the implicit priorities each group would assign to a set of specifically stated heuristics. Indeed, it has been pointed out that a stranger in a new society may become progressively more confused about the operating values of a society as he learns more about the formal statements the inhabitants make about their values. "The explicit formulations are effective guides only to those who have already so fully internalized the multitude of situational directives that they have become dulled to the . . . logical implications of the explicit value statements of the society."[37]

2. Differences in the elements of society to which they would each award power prerogatives. The historic guffaw that accompanied the assertion that, "What's good for General

---

[37] Ralph H. Turner, "Social Disorganization, Deviance, and Social Problems," *Sociology: The Progress of a Decade,* ed. Seymour Martin Lipset and Neil J. Smelser (Englewood Cliffs, N.J.: Prentice-Hall, Inc., 1961), p. 526.

Motors is good for America," is perhaps primarily attributable to the fact that it is not considered in good taste to place on public display one's own private power aspirations. The fact that the statement might or might not be true in some global societal sense was beside the point. The sight of a corporation executive betraying a possible slip of his power tongue was inevitably perceived as a possible violation of the unwritten canons of good taste.

3. Differences in the specific scenarios of situations that the two groups have in mind as they espouse their individual causes. To the stereotype of an economic "conservative" in American society, the economic situations to be dealt with are seen as consisting of firms and individuals willing and able to engage in free competition for markets, resources, and profits. Under these conditions, "government interference" is seen as a barrier to "freedom." To the stereotype of an economic "liberal," on the other hand, the situations are characterized by monopolistic control of the economic process by mammoth corporations, under conditions in which freedom of competition is impossible. To such a liberal, "government interference" can be seen as a method for insuring that freedom of competition will be permitted. People with identical value orientations can be found classified as either conservative or liberal depending upon their perception of empirical reality.

4. Differences in notions about the structure of operating units within this society. Are the human operating units motivated primarily by wishes to maximize their individual fortunes, at the expense of their neighbors if necessary? Or are they motivated primarily by codes of religion and morality to maximize the search for a more common welfare? In a specific situation, would these operating units prefer to surrender some national prerogatives rather than to insure total devastation of their own and other nations? Under what specific circumstances would they choose to press the nuclear war button or refrain from doing so?

5. Differences in perceptions of the environments within which the respective causes attempt to provide design solutions.

Is the outer world essentially hostile? Or is it peopled by persons approximately as sincere in their search for solutions as our own? Are we trying to solve only our own problems? Or are we trying to help solve problems for persons living in other countries of this world? Who is the customer?

In short, value differences are sometimes nothing more than differences in ways of looking at reality. Sometimes they consist of honest differences in opinion about the most effective way to achieve mutually agreed-upon goals. Sometimes they reflect fundamental differences in primary orientation to the world we live in. These differences may be as simple as a preference for the Martins over the Coys; they can be as complex as the choice between egoism and humanitarianism.

Probably the most distinctive characteristic of classical utopian designs is the basic "humanitarian" bent of their value structures. In Sir Thomas More's *Utopia*, the inhabitants are more concerned with the welfare of their fellow men than with furthering their individual fortunes. The phalanstery designed by Charles Fourier provides environments and procedures calculated to undo the more undesirable human consequences of unbridled individualism. And even in Francis Bacon's *New Atlantis*, where the major emphasis is presumably placed upon scientific programs, the fundamental goal of scientific activity is seen as the solution of social problems and the welfare of human beings— rather than the advancement of science for its own sake.

And perhaps the most notable difference to be found between the classical system designers and their contemporary counterparts (system engineers, data processing specialists, computer manufacturers, and system designers) consists precisely in the fact that the humanitarian bent has disappeared. The dominant value orientation of the utopian renaissance can best be described as "efficiency" rather than "humanitarianism."

The powerful appeal of the efficiency concept is a well-known and well-documented feature of contemporary Western civilization. It is more efficient to ride in an automobile than it is to walk. It is more efficient to fly in an airplane than it is to ride in an automobile. It is more efficient to use a guided missile than it is to use a manned bomber, and so on. The fundamental challenge of efficiency arises in connection with the struggle for ascendancy over man's physical environment. This struggle may be rationalized as a necessity for the survival of man. More frequently these days it is simply attributed to the sport of satisfying man's insatiable curiosity about the universe in which he finds himself. For the American schoolboy, learning to exert mastery over the mysterious forces of nature has become every bit as much a challenge as the problem of overcoming rival princes ever was for Machiavelli's Lorenzo de Medici. But just as no de Medici could seriously be expected to learn his politics from pre-Machiavellian books, it is not reasonable to expect American schoolboys to learn the facts of the utopian renaissance exclusively from contemporary computer journals and works on system engineering. The strength of Machiavelli, as the first of the modern analysts of power, consisted of the fact that, "Where others looked at the figureheads, he kept his eyes glued behind the scenes. He wanted to know what made things tick; he wanted to take the clock of the world to pieces to find out how it worked."[38]

Information necessary to take apart the clock of the contemporary world is simply not underscored in contemporary computer journals and works on system engineering, which remain devoted to the idols of physical efficiency. The central consequences of the utopian renaissance involve fundamental changes not only in the value structure of Western people, but redistributions of power concentrations made possible through the use of system control mechanisms. The resurgence of intellectual and political orientations such as "conservative" and "liberal" must be re-examined in the light of these newly emerging, altered power relationships.

Classical utopias received their impetus from a dissatisfaction with existing reality. They represented attempts to design systems more consistent with notions about what was really "good" for the mankinds they knew or dreamed about. They were unsuccessful largely because their designers, in attempting to

---

[38] Max Lerner, "Introduction to Niccolò Machiavelli," *The Prince and the Discourses* (New York: Random House, 1950), p. xxvi.

transcend the limits of their own environmental realities, severed the threads between their brave new systems and the system control or power mechanisms of their times.

Our own utopian renaissance receives its impetus from a desire to extend the mastery of man over nature. Its greatest vigor stems from a dissatisfaction with the limitations of man's existing control over his physical environment. Its greatest threat consists precisely in its potential as a means for extending the control of man over man.

INDEX